TRANSFER U.

TRANSFER U.

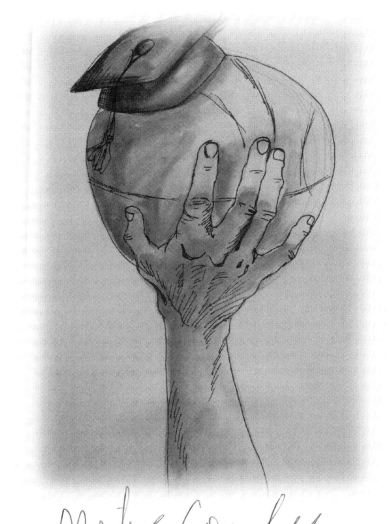

Mike Conklin

MIKE CONKLIN

Keep reading!!

Cover design and illustrations by Georgia Gump
Instagram: @jamiedoeart

Book design by Maureen Cutajar
www.gopublished.com

ISBN-13: 978-0-9980283-0-9
ISBN-10: 0-9980283-0-4

FOREWORD

A young and ambitious high school basketball coach in a small, rural community once gave me his idea of success. "You know you've arrived when you're coaching in a town big enough to have a Holiday Inn."

You can't make up this stuff. Or can you? We know truth often is funnier than fiction. Nowhere can this be more obvious than in the worlds of academia and athletics, where ambition, status, and ego often are the day's orders.

With *Transfer U.*, I decided to take the high road. I went with fiction over truth. There's a fine line between them, of course, and everything gets boosted a bit in my story by using some familiar names, institutions, and facts to provide context. But I guarantee the narratives and descriptions are products purely of my imagination.

ACKNOWLEDGMENTS

Writing for audiences is a collaborative effort. Working at The Chicago Tribune gave me access to many worlds, big and small. My newspaper editors and other colleagues, too many to name, created a perfect environment for gathering, discussing, and reporting stories.

While I no longer work in a newsroom, that does not mean I lack good places to write. My office, various libraries, and coffee shops work well and, throughout the process, I could not have a better touchstone than my wife, Diane. Few people can be more dedicated to books.

To understand writing, it is important to be a reader. In addition to belonging to three book clubs, Diane's yearly calendar includes volunteering many hours on four used book sales that total over $500,000 for good causes. Her observations, input, and support are invaluable. She knows books.

Laurie Stein, a public historian, writer, researcher, and, fortuitously for me, former sports editor of her college newspaper, gave my manuscript a thorough read. She offered needed edits, corrections, and continuity.

If you judge a book by its cover, I am in great shape. I was also lucky enough to get Georgia Gump, a young artist just out of Cornell College (Ia.) to work with me in designing it. She is very talented with a bright future.

While I drew on my own work experiences for Transfer U., there have been plenty of people who provided assists in numerous ways. They did this providing answers to questions, anecdotes, inspiration themselves, or simple encouragement. Thanks to: Jerry Anderson, James Elsener, Steve Miller, Alan Stone, Jonieta Stone, Marla Krause, Curt Tobin, Tom Beck, Mike Imrem, Mitch Engel, Fred Jackson, Tony Plaut, Adrienne Fawcett, Neil Milbert and the Legends Book Club.

Prologue

THE REGULAR WEDNESDAY night card game was in full swing at Whitey's Tavern.

Once a week, except in summer when students home from college overran the place, Gil Munson, Swede Andersen, Frank Gralla, and Guy Troyer gathered to play euchre.

They experimented variously with poker, hearts, spades, and gin rummy over the years. "We tried bridge for a few weeks, too," Frank once recalled to a casual observer. "Didn't fly. Only Guy could figure how to keep score. That meant we were screwed when he couldn't make it."

Whitey's was a made-for-Hollywood setting, but only if the movie needed scenes from, say, the 1950s. Sort of a James Dean thing.

It was a solitary, wooden ramshackle building next to the Tippecanoe River in southern Indiana. It sat on a high, concrete foundation with honest-to-God, but unused in decades, hitching rails for horses lining the front walkway under an overhanging roof.

A short stroll from the front door, there was a wooden-plank bridge long ago declared unsafe—and closed—for motorized vehicles over the Tippecanoe. Pedestrians were welcome, however, and walking the quarter-mile, steel-spanned structure became a local attraction.

It was not uncommon for marriage to be proposed on the old bridge. Two weddings had been held on it in recent years, funeral ashes frequently got sprinkled into the river from it and, at least three times, drunks stumbled off it into the river.

"No one's drowned yet, that I know of," Whitey proudly proclaims.

The tavern, in the middle of nowhere even by rural Indiana standards, offered a small selection of groceries and modest short-order kitchen fare.

It was the lone business for miles in summertime, typically when Gil, Swede, Frank, and Guy took a break from their weekly game, bluegrass concerts were held in the parking lot.

Inside there was a pool table in one corner not far from an authentic wood-burning, pot-belly stove. The stove hasn't been used for nearly 10 years, not since a first-time, beer-numb visitor—not realizing it was the real deal—backed into it lining up a shot on the 8-ball.

He burned his ass so bad he ran out the door with pants smoking and jumped into the river. He suffered second degree burns.

The stranger threatened to sue Whitey, but quickly dropped his case when card-playing regular Guy, a lawyer in real life and eyewitness, threatened to counter-sue on the tavern's behalf. Impaired pool playing?

"There!!" declared Frank, on this night slapping down a low trump card to take the last trick. "Game, set, and match boys. I believe that makes me a winner. Who deals? Somebody shuffle."

Amidst the usual grumbling, razzing, and Swede getting up to hit the bathroom while cards were dealt, a cold autumn gush of air rushed into Whitey's when the front door opened.

Everyone froze.

Through the door, a very tall—maybe 7-foot—Chinese young adult male emerged after ducking to avoid banging his head on the frame. He pulled himself upright, looked around, and processed what he observed. Then, he retreated back through the door.

A 7-foot Chinaman in Whitey's?

Just as everyone burst into excited conversation over this strange interruption, they again froze—this time with Swede just about to enter the men's restroom—when the front door again opened.

Led by the very tall person just observed, seven additional Chinese youth, including one girl who could not be more than 5-feet tall, trooped into the tavern behind him. They quietly and carefully took seats.

Everyone stared at the strangers. After closely studying the menu on the wall and much whispering (in Chinese), the girl got up, placed the order at the bar in perfect English, and rejoined the group.

Whitey was quite relieved to see it was soft drinks-only with their burgers and fries. He had no clue how to ask for ID.

With the two tables in the middle of the tavern occupied by the Chinese, the atmosphere then lowered to quiet whispers and quick, curious glances from the other clientele.

This was especially hard on Gil, Frank, Swede and Guy, whose chatter and kibitzing was a regular part of their card game. Finally, Guy, a lawyer with an engaging manner, couldn't take it.

He got up, walked over to their table, and, addressing the visitors, asked in the politest tone he could muster: "I don't mean to be rude and we truly welcome everyone here, but who are you people?"

The tall youth who first opened the door stood, stuck out his hand, shook Guy's hand (crushed it, actually), and, in impeccable English, said: "We are from China. We play basketball."

I China Syndromes

1

I can breathe

AS MY AIRPLANE circled above, my destination city below easily could be mistaken for San Francisco.

Its skyscraper-laden, urban sprawl lined a huge bay. The bridges that connected both sides were busy with traffic. There were ferry boats crisscrossing the water. They made stops on islands as well as both sides of the mainland.

Then, as our airplane dipped closer, I saw palm trees, white sand beaches, swimmers, surfers, and sun-worshipers on the edges of the water.

Scratch San Francisco, and make it Miami?

No, as incongruous as it might seem to American tourists, this was China.

The bay was on the South China Sea and the target city was Xiamen, a city of 3.8 million in the southeastern province of Fujian.

Every year Xiamen is voted one of China's most habitable cities. It is a popular vacation destination throughout southeast Asia and within the country itself. The port is one of Asia's busiest for international commerce. It hosts many business conferences and conventions.

Xiamen (pronounced SHA-men) also is a university town. I would learn that the largest, Xiamen University, was one of the country's leading schools.

This was why I was on this trip. The school was to become my new home, where I had landed a teaching position.

While I experienced none of the smog that plagues Beijing and other parts of this huge, densely-populated nation, I did not arrive in Xiamen completely Scot-free of elements.

My scheduled two-hour layover in Tokyo became a six-hour layover because of a typhoon passing through Fujian Province. A typhoon. Now THAT was unsettling.

As a result of the delay, this meant I would fly very late into an un-known, huge city that just experienced a powerful, deadly wind storm. I did not know one word in a Chinese dialect and, to sweeten things, knew nothing about accommodations arranged by my new employer.

"Taxi! Taxi!" How do you say that in Mandarin? I did not have a clue. I wouldn't even know where to go if I successfully got one to stop. Was there a Holiday Inn Express? Maybe my Uber app would work.

At the time, I was a newly-minted possessor of a Master of Fine Arts in creative writing from the University of Iowa. The program was a very rigorous, two-year residency effort.

To get admitted, I needed to graduate with honors from a small, but tough, four-year liberal arts school, Lake Forest College in the Chicago suburbs, and where I had been a varsity athlete.

Now, it was get-a-job-and-pay-off-loans time. Naturally, there were no solid employment offers.

This led to taking a temporary position to teach communication courses for a Chinese university in Xiamen, an opening I read about on a bulletin board outside the office of my then-advisor, David James.

On impulse, I applied. I never gave it much thought at the time.

Imagine my surprise when I got an offer. What the heck. Writing is communicating, right? This seemed like a break from the usual job drill, and a little adventure to boot.

You had to think teaching in a foreign country would look good in my quest for a permanent college job in the U.S. This was my ultimate goal.

Back to geography: Xiamen's 3.8 million residents would make it one of the largest cities in the United States, but not enough to crack China's top 20.

Naturally, like most card-carrying Americans, Xiamen was a mystery to me. Never heard of the place before seeing it on the bulletin board flyer.

Located on the South China Sea not far from Vietnam and with Taiwan close as well, it was gorgeous with its tropical setting. The bay included a large, historic island named Gulangyu.

This was not the China everyone back in the U.S. thought they knew. Put away your gas masks.

The local culture was as welcoming as the environment. The city was a Chinese port declared by the government decades ago as an economic free zone—like Hong Kong.

This made Xiamen a popular place for tourists and business people. Visiting teachers? If my reception in the Xiamen airport was an indication, my experience would be just fine. And well-organized.

It was 5 p.m. local time (and God knows what time for my body) when my Air China flight finally landed. Waiting for me at the gate was this: Two earnest, young Chinese students holding up a placard with my name: "Phillip James Doyle."

Cool.

I always wondered what that experience would be like, greeted in an airport with your name on a sign. I felt like a VIP. What, no photographers?

My greeters were polite, bowed when I identified myself, introduced themselves as Ling and Liu, and agreed to call me "Flip," which everyone did back in the States.

We were off in their car just as soon as they claimed—and insisted on carrying—my baggage.

Yes, I could get used to this.

We crept through crowded streets—rush hour?—crammed with small shops. I could see tree branches on the ground and some broken windows, but that was the only evidence of the typhoon.

We arrived at my apartment hotel located on the edge of the campus where I figured to be teaching. It was a very tall building, maybe 20 stories and located just inside the main gate with a nice view of the university.

We were greeted by two porters, and I was fast asleep in my bed before I could unpack. The last thing I remember was Ling—or was it Liu?—saying they'd return in the morning.

Up to now, total efficiency. This seemed OK.

Red carpet treatment

"JUST CALL ME Bunny." Bunny?

In a country of over a billion people in which everyone seemed to be named Fong, Fang, or Wang, the dean of the College of Communication at Xiamen University—a woman presiding over 21 full professors with PhDs, 43 more faculty striving for full professor status, 25 assorted adjuncts, 15 administrative staff, 3,986 students, and the occasional foreign part-timer (that would be me) who wandered through—wanted to be called Bunny?

OK, who was I to argue? Her real name was Wang Li. She was my opening appointment on what figured to be a busy first day.

It would be devoted to getting acclimated with this exotic, sprawling Xiamen University in an exotic, new city in a part of the world totally new to me that, just for good measure, was in a time zone with a 12-hour difference from my home in the U.S. Midwest.

"So, Mr. Doyle, we are very pleased to have you teaching here this summer," said Bunny, as we moved to more comfortable chairs facing each other. "We like to extend the hand of friendship to our visitors. Would you like some tea?"

Twenty minutes later, I cannot say I knew a whole lot more about my big adventure. We concluded with Ms. Li, or Bunny, handing to me a very thick booklet with rules and regulations governing campus life.

Here was one that kind of got my attention:

"Teachers should make every effort to improve their teaching and carry out proper preparation for each class. They should be neatly dressed when in class and be polite in their use of language."

I was ushered back into the reception area—and greeted by Ling and Liu, my go-to guys for the remainder of the day.

"First, we will walk around the campus and show important buildings to you," said Liu. "These will be the library, the concert hall, the computer laboratory, dining hall, and arts and science center.

"You will be very impressed," he added. "We are very proud of them. Only our best architects designed them."

Naturally, I wanted to learn where I would be teaching.

What facilities would be available in my classroom?

Would my carefully-prepared PowerPoint slides be operable?

Could I show films?

Where were the restrooms?

Was there a restroom?

"We will show your place for educating students tomorrow morning," said Liu, the chattier of the two.

This seemed a bit tight—my first classes were scheduled to start in two days, but, what the heck, when in China….. go with the flow.

The tour did prove enlightening. This university was a big deal, I began to realize.

Turns out the Chinese have official rankings for their universities. Students are assigned to them based on results from their national, entrance examinations.

Hey, no SAT tutoring fees for Junior. No entrance essays. No application deposits. I know a lot of parents in the States who could go for that.

In a country with over a billion people, Xiamen was ranked No. 12 on the university list. This also sounded pretty good to me.

I did not speak any Chinese whatsoever, though I could handle chopsticks with ease. I was assured my students all spoke fluent English (as promised on the bulletin board brochure I first read in Iowa City).

Just outside the school's main gate was Nanpoutuo Temple, a huge

Buddhist facility founded in the Tang Dynasty—thank you, Wikipedia—sometime in the 7th or 8th century.

There was a constant stream of worshipers and tourists to the temple, in addition to chanting, incense-burning Buddhist monks throughout the grounds. I was told thousands and thousands of Chinese made annual pilgrimages to this very sacred site.

University enrollment was just under 45,000 students, which made it smaller than only a few U.S. schools. The school was founded in 1921 by a Chinese businessman who got his start in the rice business.

After surviving the Japanese occupation, disputes among warlords, Western imperialism, Communist re-organization, various purges, and re-locations, the university took flight in the 1960s when it was officially declared a "state key university."

Hard to believe, but this meant almost the entire 1,200-acre campus—a careful scheme of large and small complementary buildings, small patches of green ringing a central square with crisscrossing sidewalks, palm trees, several coffee shops with outdoor seating, ponds (with lily pads and geese), specialty-food vendors, book stalls, and more bicycle racks than I knew existed—was put together in only a few decades.

I knew streets in Chicago that took longer to have potholes filled.

In the distance, I could see space designated for a dozen or so outdoor basketball courts. There were some furious-looking games underway, too. Bicycles were everywhere, and unlocked.

It looked like it was going to be interesting teaching here. Should I look into extending my stay? I was anxious to see where I was to teach. Hopefully it overlooked this campus scene.

It didn't.

3

Sea legs

LING AND LIU, my personal Yin and Yang, were at my door promptly at 8 the next morning. They would give me an advanced peek of a classroom I was itchy to see.

That was the good news.

The bad news?

Lou asked, "Do you get seasick, Mister Doyle?"

Err, well, no. What's that got to do with anything? I thought we were going to see my classroom.

We were, but here was how we had to get there—and what became a daily, weekday commute during my teaching term.

Step 1: We caught a campus bus reserved for faculty at a stop across from my apartment-hotel a block from the main campus I toured yesterday. Fifteen minutes later, the bus pulled up to a pier on the bay. There, we filed through a long and narrow building before exiting and piled onto a ferry boat at the opposite end.

Step 2: We spent 25 minutes on the mostly open-air boat (fortunately it did not rain this day), passed several islands, rounded a corner of the bay, and—thankfully—remained within sight of the shoreline. Finally, we pulled up to one of two small islands hugging the mainland.

Step 3: Our little group exited the ferry, boarded a bus, and, passing a golf course under construction, drove to the opposite side of the island I estimated to be maybe three square miles.

There, we were greeted by a complex of four, high-rise, concrete, and sterile towers that housed classrooms. They dwarfed a cluster of smaller, concrete buildings that were dormitories, dining facilities, and administrative offices.

Also, there were more outdoor basketball courts and a small soccer pitch on the grounds.

Large signs in front of the four classroom buildings told us their catchy names: Building No. 1; Building No. 2; Building No. 3; and—you guessed it—Building No. 4.

Ling, Liu, and I got out at Building No. 2.

Next came five flights of stairs. The elevators were not working. There was no air conditioning. I thought I was in decent shape, having been a college athlete before grad school, but *whew*. Also, I got sweaty because we were in the middle of a tropical summer.

The classroom was huge. A small auditorium, really. There were desks for 75 students and, important to me, there was a projector and screen with enough capacity to show my slides and DVDs. I was good-to-go.

Ling and Liu showed the rest of the premises.

This included a faculty dining hall and getting an introduction to the department administrator, who handed me another thick brochure—in six different languages—of more rules and regulations.

The island, it turned out, was where foreign teachers on temporary duty like me typically got assigned. Furthermore, our students were all first or second year levels. Their goal was to "graduate" to the main campus.

So, my teaching would require a daily commute of one-hour in each direction. This trek consisted of rides on two buses and a boat.

Well, bring it on. I was pumped.

Not just numbers

WHEN I LOOK back, it's obvious I got as much out of my time teaching in China as my kids. The experience, as silly as it may sound, was an education.

The classes were huge (I thought), numbering 50-60 students. There were no teachers assistants, though I came to lean on several of the more energetic, communicative kids for help.

Jingfei ("call me 'Jing,' everyone else does") Zhang, one of my most inquisitive students, eventually became my de facto TA and all-around helper in and out of the classroom.

I'm not sure who adopted whom, but, as I piece it together, she became vital in my improbable tale.

Bright and funny, Jing earned a seat in the front row. In addition to speaking English better than many students on U.S. campuses, she was tech-savvy.

And there *were* early glitches.

What's that old saying? Necessity is the mother of invention?

For starters, the student rosters were in Chinese. Every name looked to me as if it was in Egyptian hieroglyphics. Each student was numbered, but I had no idea of their identities.

Certainly I was not going to ask a question, look at my list, and randomly call on "No. 39" for an answer. I mean China was a nation of one billion people or more, but they weren't going to be mere numbers to me.

A light bulb went off!

The roster was passed around the classroom and each student got asked to put a name they wanted to be called next to their number. I told them to let it rip, have some fun and, laughing and smiling, they complied.

Some of the names returned: *Lady Gaga, Confucius, Taylor, Beyonce, Pierre, Mack The Knife, Frankenstein, The Donald, Oprah, Yao Ming, Sherlock, Spike Lee, Big Red, Justin, Mickey Mouse, LeBron, Rambo, Elvis....*

The kids had insatiable curiosity. Every class ended with many coming to my lectern to pepper me with questions about the United States. Movies, music, fashion, politics, and sports were the most popular subjects.

Why did Brad and Angelina split?

What are the best American colleges?

Was I Republican or Democrat?

Whatever happened to Michael Jordan?

Did I shop at Wal-Mart or Target?

Lots of National Basketball Association fans, too, judging by the paraphernalia worn to classes. The Golden State Warriors seemed to be most popular. Other t-shirts ranged from "University of Pink" and "I'm With Stupid" to "Coed Naked Golf" and "Property of University of Southern California Athletic Department."

It does not take long to learn China, or for sure this part—Fujian Province—was not simply "the Yellow hordes" imagined by Americans.

While the majority of my students were of Han ethnicity, which makes up most of the country, there also were Zhuang, Uyghur, Manchu, and Mongols. They came in all sizes, shapes, hues, and accents.

Jingfei helped me sort it out and, in being her unrelenting cheery self, never displayed bias toward any classmates on her part.

Rule No. 4 in my university rules & regulation book:

"Teachers may not discriminate against any person on grounds of race, color, culture, religion, national origin, gender, sexual orientation or disability."

I did learn everyone's English was not as good as I was led to believe. Some could read and write the language perfectly, but had no ear or oral ability. Others could understand and speak it fluently, but possessed no writing or reading skills.

Since American films were a big part of my courses, I struck upon this formula: I ran English closed-captions with them despite the fact they already were speaking in English. This is what we in the business call full-service teaching.

The most popular screening? This came in a segment I did on American-style TV journalism, when, in what had to be a premiere for this country, I showed "China Syndrome."

The students were enthralled watching Jane Fonda and Michael Douglas run all over California. But they were puzzled, too.

"Mr. Professor," said Jingfei, "I liked the film very much, but I am confused. Many of us thought this would be about China. Did we miss something?"

This took some careful explaining. About how China Syndrome was merely a catchphrase for a nuclear meltdown that burns a hole through U.S. soil to China. I tried my best. Well, maybe you had to be there.

5

Dragon boat races, anyone?

ONE OF THE big, early challenges in China for any visitor from North America is overcoming the time zone difference. What day was it here, in the U.S., or, for that matter, anywhere?

Every mid-afternoon for the first few weeks, my body simply shut down. But I learned if I took a nap, this made it difficult to fall asleep later when it was time to retire.

I spent a number of nights after one of those daytime naps tossing and turning when I should have been sleeping. I found myself up and ready to go at 3 a.m. more than a few times.

Determined to work my way through the time warp, the plan was simple: Don't take a nap. Avoid returning to my apartment following the last class, and explore.

For starters, there were South China Sea white sand beaches and palm trees within walking distance.

One sandy strip featured a dozen or so high-end hotels, a boardwalk, restaurants, and beautiful lobbies with gift shops where I could buy a daily Asian edition of the NY Times, grab a chair, sip coffee, and read. This was living large, in my book.

On one excursion, I bumped into Jingfei and pals, a few of whom were my students. They were quick to list points of interest. They wanted me—the Westerner—not to miss anything and took me to a few sites that afternoon.

"It is only fair," said Jing. "We ask you so much about your America. Let us show you our Xiamen."

Well, unless I missed it, the closest I could come in my "rules & regulations" brochure covering socializing with students was Rule No. 5:

Teachers must respect the worth, culture and dignity of each and every individual, including exercising courtesy and restraint in the event of any conflict, and encourage the all-round development of the students.

Turned out one section of the campus—a spacious alley between buildings—was reserved for twice-a-week, student-driven flea markets.

I saw items I guarantee never would be found in the U.S. Cheaper, too. Lots of bootleg DVDs and CDs. On this first visit, I could not resist buying a used Chinese Army cap with a red star worn—the vendor told me—in the Korean War.

There also was a very cool student art gallery with a coffee shop that became a regular stop for me. Caffeine was good, but, as a popular gathering spot, tables could be difficult to get.

On Tuesday afternoons, joint student-faculty musical ensembles performed on an outdoor stage at one corner of the campus square. These were popular, too.

That temple outside the main entrance to the campus?

It consisted of acres and acres of paths, small chapels, burning candles and benches spread across a mountainside. As a neighbor to a bustling, large university in a dense city, this site became a good spot to think and meditate.

My favorite side trips were to Gulangyu Island, where Jing guided me multiple times. I could get off my ferry boat after a morning of teaching, jump on another commuter vessel at the same pier, and be there in minutes.

No motorized vehicles were allowed on the square-mile surface. The commercial section was full of small shops, outdoor cafes, a large hotel, and a Starbucks. It was reachable by foot on a walkway leading up from the water.

Gulangyu's history was fascinating. It complemented Xiamen's reputation as an important global destination, where rivers flowing into the bay could take visitors deep into the Chinese interior.

The island was where many prominent international businessmen and diplomats resided in large mansions, some of which had been turned into small hotels and B&Bs.

There were Christian churches, mixed with temples, and a concert facility in which most of China's concert pianists came to train and perform.

One Saturday, I watched dragon boat races around the island.

CHAPTER

6

Hoops

THE SATURDAY AFTERNOON campus concert on the green square was impressive.

It lasted nearly two hours and, as someone explained, celebrated the Ming Dynasty in China's history. Well, OK. Bring on the Ming.

I did not understand a word they were singing. Nevertheless, it was impossible not to appreciate the colorful costumes, indigenous musical instruments, dancing and singing.

There were several hundred spectators. I was there because Jing, with several classmates, insisted it was a must-see.

She pointed out the Ming was the dynasty in which the Great Wall and Forbidden City were built in China. It was interesting to see young college students attentive for a performance celebrating national culture. There was no mosh pit.

This was one more stop on Jing's cultural tour for me outside the classroom. She accompanied me whenever it was possible. When it was not, she "assigned" that job to one of her pals.

"You must see everything. We do not get many American visitors in Xiamen. The Great Wall does not stretch this far," she added.

Whether or not they realized it, Ling and Liu, my original guide dudes, had been replaced.

When the music was over at this particular concert, we headed to the student art gallery and its coffee shop. We never quite made it, however.

During the Saturday concert, the noise at the other end of the campus square—loud cheering and whistling—had been a growing distraction.

Several hundred students ringed two side-by-side basketball courts. Teams in full uniforms charged up and down outdoor, vulcanized rubber surfaces. Intriguing.

Basketball was part of my DNA. I hated to give it up my senior year at Lake Forest College, but I had to get my academic record in order for graduate school at Iowa.

The coach was not happy at unexpectedly losing a two-year starter at point guard, either. "Have a nice writing career, Bub," he said, after I broke the news.

After the concert, we muscled our way to the front row of standees for a closer look at the basketball and a loose, game ball quickly bounced our way. I grabbed it and, on sudden impulse, let fly with a jump shot of some 50 feet.

You guessed it. The ball—and I am not making this up—swished cleanly through the hoop.

The roar would've drowned out the concert if the music had not stopped. A small crowd gathered around me, high-fiving, hugging, and cheering.

"Mr. Doyle, you are a hero," said Jing. "You are a great basketball player. You never say this. You are—what you call—All-American. Yes?"

No.

I explained to everyone it was a lucky shot, maybe one in 50? No one wanted to believe me.

Basketball was an American sport and I was American. That's all that mattered. They wanted a star. I made a remarkable shot. End of story. A dozen or so additional students followed us to the art gallery. I felt like the Pied Piper.

Our crowd was so large that, when we reached the doors, we would've been a distraction. I excused myself and retreated to my apartment on the other side of the square, leaving my entourage in the lobby.

This may not have been the shot heard 'round the world, but it definitely was the shot heard 'round Xiamen University's campus.

Suiting up

WORD SPREAD QUICKLY of "the shot." When my class met on Monday, everyone rose and applauded as I entered the room. Someone scribbled on the blackboard, "Mr. All-American teacher."

"You must understand," Jing explained. "Basketball is very popular at Xiamen, on the campus and in the city. There are many followers of your National Basketball Association here. This is probably our No. 1 sport. Soccer, not so much. Maybe No. 2."

There was no intercollegiate competition in China as we know it in the U.S. Instead, nearly a thousand male and female Xiamen students played in well-organized intramural leagues.

Many players were very skilled, playing at a level equal to—or greater than—what I competed against in U.S. small-college ranks. Off the university campus, there was a two-tiered Xiamen city league with 12 club teams.

Some clubs took it very seriously, importing players from abroad, paying small salaries, traveling to Pacific Rim tournaments, and with corporate sponsors giving off-season jobs to those on their roster.

The powerhouse in the club league was sponsored by one of China's most popular beverages, Tsingtao Beer. "Rah, yeaaaay Tsingtao !! Give me a T.…… Give me a beer!"

For me, personally, things quieted after a few days following "the shot." Then, quickly it picked up again.

I had an offer. Not an offer of a college-teaching job in the U.S., but an offer to play in the university's intramural leagues.

The Xiamen season was nearing its mid-point, but this turned out to be a good exercise—literally. I needed to drop a few pounds.

My team was in the Faculty Division and called Crouching Tigers. Others in the division were Dragon Fire, Raining Flowers, Buddhist Bombardiers, Carp Flying Fiercely, and Mao's Marauders.

Some good friendships were developed, both on the court and afterward over drinks and food. Almost all faculty teams had a foreigner or two like me on the roster.

Expectations were great, especially when the foreigner was American. Few lived up to those expectations.

I held my own, though.

Some strategies and plays I suggested to my Crouching Tiger teammates actually worked. In the process, my language skills expanded. Now I could call "time out," "pass the ball," and curse referees in two Chinese dialects.

The competition was fun, though faculty squads generally got drilled in cross-over games against students, who saw it as a great loss of face to lose to their teachers.

Unfortunately, my Crouching Tigers were much better at crouching than jumping, running, and shooting. We won five games. We played 20.

Each week seemed to bring a new surprise in and out of the classroom during my Xiamen stay. Basketball, both as an observer and participant, was a most unexpected, but pleasant, one.

I knew how shared experiences with teammates in the U.S. formed strong bonds. Now, the bonding seemed even more meaningful when it was with teammates from a different nation on a previously unknown (to me) continent.

As my year of Xiamen teaching neared an end, I knew I would miss this experience. For sure, we would stay in touch through social media.

8

Farewell dinner

JING WOULD NOT let me leave Xiamen without meeting her family. She insisted I come to her home for dinner. This sounded good.

My stay in the city and university was fascinating up to this point. It could be life-changing, actually, if I did not land a suitable U.S. college job. I would consider strongly returning to teach here.

But entering the final week of my stay, it did occur as I packed that it would be interesting to meet a family in a domestic setting.

This was a missing ingredient in my stay, an opportunity to take yet another peek behind the China curtain. I had not been inside a local household or met any of my students' families.

Hey, come to think of it, I had not eaten a home-cooked meal for months. I jumped at her invitation.

Meat loaf and mashed potatoes? Lasagna and salad?

Then Jing told me dishes that might be considered appropriate by her family for such an important occasion. These included Shark fin, sauteed seaweed, Yak Meat Dumplings, stuffed snails, fried silkworms, and, right about here, I interrupted.

Uhhh, Jing, please tell your family not to knock themselves out for me. I'm a simple man with simple tastes. Fried rice would be fine.

As it developed, the evening was a nice capper to my stay.

The food was delicious, though I was not inquisitive. The final, sweet dish was a serving of something brown and crispy, which was quite tasty (and later learned was fried Cicada shells).

The Zhang family lived not far from campus, requiring a short taxi ride. Their home was four sparsely furnished, small rooms in a high-rise (maybe 1200 square feet) with a view directly into a twin tower on the opposite side of a courtyard.

It was in Siming District, highly urban with many neighboring tall buildings overlooking Gulangyu Island less than a mile away in the bay. Their building was part of a smaller sub-district, Zhonghua, in which grassroots government was administered.

The days of Chinese thought-police tapping telephones and peeking through keyholes did not exist as far as I could tell. At least it certainly seemed the case on campus, where students seemed free and easy.

Still, when I thought about this, it was difficult to imagine what my students' parents and grandparents experienced in their lifetimes.

The Great Depression, maybe. World War II and Korean War? Hey, the Chinese were in those wars, too. The Japanese occupation of China before and during World War II was horrific by anyone's measure.

You needed a scorecard to tell China's political purges apart after Mao and the Communists took control in the late 1940s. The older generations, having endured so many upheavals, generally felt it safer never to be outspoken or critical of their country around strangers.

Our little group consisted of Jing's father (Zhang Wei), mother (Na Li), and younger brother (Zhang Yong), who, a year away from testing to enter higher ed, was an avid basketball player and follower of U.S. college teams Duke, UCLA and, inexplicably, Montana State.

Jing explained beforehand her father worked as an assembly-line supervisor in a company that made sunglasses. Her mother owned a small tea and coffee shop only a few blocks from home.

I learned the Zhang family got caught in Chinese cultural revolutionary crosshairs. The factionalism in this nation made U.S. politics seem like name-calling on a grade school playground.

Wei's father (Jing's grandfather) was a significant, mid-level Communist functionary, important enough to be a member of the official party that welcomed U.S. President Richard Nixon on his groundbreaking 1972 visit.

He's in the background of photographs used by mainstream media of the historic occasion, standing a few dignitaries away from a smiling Henry Kissinger. Reverently, I was shown pictures of that historic day.

But grandpa found himself in the wrong place a few years later. When the Red Guards ran amuck, he was judged "an enemy of the movement." There was no jury to deliberate the matter.

He was transported to a farm collective in a distant, rural region with his family. At the time, this included Jing's grandmother, father, and an uncle.

Thus Wei, Jing's father, was interrupted in the early years as a very promising college student in literature. He never regained academic traction. His father did his best, tutoring him in subjects not taught in the primitive school available in their new, spartan home.

"My father was a college professor in history before me, very much an idealist before he became active in politics," said Zei. "He strongly believed education was the most important thing China could do for its citizens."

The grandfather's tutoring sessions were popular. They expanded to include other displaced students like his son in the small village the Zhang family was assigned, located in the far northwest Gansu Province.

Zei met Li in these gatherings. They married and eventually worked their way to an urban setting.

They were lucky it was Xiamen, an ancient, economic-free zone for nearly a century. The city was influenced centuries before by foreigners aboard trade ships that docked and unloaded in the harbor.

Xiamen's standard of living was among the highest in China. Jobs were plentiful. Gulangyu Island and the university were cultural hubs.

Jing's family felt relaxed enough with me, their first-ever foreign guest, to be candid about life and times in the most populated nation in the world. They spoke from personal experience.

Their stories and descriptions should have been taped and played in every world history class in the U.S., it occurred to me later. This was the real deal. It was a privilege to be trusted in this way.

A confident Jing contributed to the dialogue, too. The parents glowed with pride over her self-assured remarks, which showed equal measures curiosity and truths that belied her youth.

Yong, her 17-year old, younger brother, seemed a bit bored by it all, periodically checking for, and sending, texts—and in the process drawing frowns from his parents. He did perk up when the subject turned to basketball.

"My daughter tells me you were an illustrious player in America," said Zei, in an attempt to get Yong involved in the conversation. "That you played at a very high level of competition at a university named Wake Forest. I have heard of this very good school."

No, no, I corrected.

"The school was Lake Forest, not Wake Forest. A good school in the classroom, but not so good on the basketball floor. It is understandable they get mistaken for each other. They are separated by only one letter."

This drew laughter, though Jing's was a bit forced. Clearly she thought it a loss of face to have mistaken the two U.S. schools. I am sure she made a silent promise this oversight never would be repeated.

As we wound down, and I stole glances at my watch, Zei suggested we finish the evening with the two of us stepping outside to smoke cigarettes. He said the women in the family did not approve of this to be done in the apartment, something he noted with a cautious look to his wife, Li.

Obviously he wanted to say something in private to me. I was correct. I took two puffs, managed not to cough at this rare experience, and he turned to face me.

"I want you to know," Zei said, "that my daughter has great respect for you. She tells me she has learned much. She is in only her first year at the university, but already she feels there will not be another professor like you. I want to issue my gratitude for this attention."

The father went on to say he and Li will sacrifice everything for Jing to have education and opportunities they missed. Like her grandfather, he felt education was the key to success.

She is especially interested—consumed, Zei added—by Western Civilization, especially the U.S. Her great goal is to visit there someday.

His daughter is bright and teachable, I told him. Jing ranks very favorably, both academically and socially, with students in America. She has a good future at whatever is pursued.

If and when I managed to get a full-time college teaching position in the U.S., I would be quite mindful of her. She would be an asset on any campus.

"That is very considerate, but, you see, there are special challenges here," said Zei, his eyes looking down, his smile disappearing, and a slight clearing of his throat before the explanation.

Jing, it turned out, was a "missing girl."

Here began an indelible lesson for me in Chinese history.

She was born at a time the Communist government enforced a rigid one-child-per-family policy. If the expected baby was not male, an abortion took place. If birth occurred and the infant was female, she was separated from the mother and consigned to a state-run orphanage.

This was China's then ham-fisted way of dealing with what was seen as a gender-imbalance in the population. The policy lasted for several decades.

Many parents, like Zei and Li, went ahead with the birth. They simply did not report or register their daughter with officials. They had another child with hopes of a male, which was Yong.

This deception was easier to accomplish in remote regions, the father continued, but it also meant the female child led a shadow existence. The parents shielded her from events that came with official scrutiny.

The government finally relaxed policies in time for Jing to start formal education at middle school level. Thanks to home schooling, Zei pointed out—proudly—she got up to speed in little time. Not everyone was so lucky.

Jing was one of millions of Chinese "missing girls" to suddenly appear on the official register. No one knows the exact number. Bookkeeping and compliance in China, despite what outsiders may think, are not meticulous.

Zei explained the government, overwhelmed by this surge, granted what loosely could be called a general "pardon" for these girls. Back on the rolls, they became citizens.

"This is very good for Jing," said her father. "She does not really know that much about what happened because she was young. Her mother and I do not talk about this in front of her. We never want her to worry."

Worry?

"We are not confident, not when you lived through so much like we have," he explained. "In China, things can be taken away as quickly as they are granted. We do not know if the past could become trouble for her.

"The political winds change in a hurry here."

9

Exit interview

MY BAGS WERE packed and Ling and Liu picked me up in plenty of time to catch what would be a mind-numbing, 20-something hour return to the United States. The flight path actually took us over the North Pole.

In fact, Ling and Liu did not take me directly to the Xiamen Airport. "What's up, boys? This day is going to be long enough as it is." No answer.

We headed straight to the central administration building, where Wang Li wanted to have a little chat. You remember? The dean of the College of Communication? Bunny?

This was another quick, efficient meeting. After tea, biscuits, and perfunctory salutations, she wanted an assessment—brief, preferably—of my stay.

This was easy. In what brought more than a polite smile, she appeared to like my observation that there was as much to learn outside the classroom for me as my students hopefully learned inside it.

"This is very good to hear," she said. "You should know I heard many positive things about your teaching. You would be most welcome to return."

The dean went on to say that Xiamen, unlike other universities in China, has a more global outlook. Recently it opened a branch campus in Malaysia, the first Chinese school to do this outside its borders.

"Our mission is to create a truly international university, one in which people from many nations gather to learn from each other academically and culturally as well," she said.

"There is much interest in the United States, especially among students. I am sure you noticed. My understanding is that you were very popular in the classroom. We hope to create many exchanges with American colleges."

Well, hey, it all sounded good to me. But I had an airplane to catch and told her I had just one, final question to ask.

What's with the name Bunny? Aren't you Wang Li?

At first, this drew a blank look. Then, a smile slowly grew.

"Oh, you mean 'Bunny' as in what some people call me? My other name? Not everyone does, of course, only those who know me well and a few who do not."

The dean went on to explain she was born in China's 'Year of the Rabbit,' but quickly added—with a smile—that she would not reveal the exact year.

"You must know that in one of China's periods of growth, families were encouraged to have only one child. You also must know that it was not considered good fortune to have girls. Later, it was forbidden.

"When I was born, my father saw me the first time and said, 'You are born in the Year of the Rabbit, so you are my bunny.'"

Later during a layover in the Beijing airport, I learned on Google that the Chinese Zodiac's 12-year animal cycle also includes snakes, goats, monkeys, dragons and pigs.

You had to figure it was the dean's good fortune to be born in the Year of the Rabbit.

I would miss China. Hopefully, I would return some day. Who knew?

10

Mixing it up

LESS THAN 24 HOURS after returning to the U.S., I was ready to book a return flight to Xiamen and take my Master of Fine Arts degree in creative writing with me.

Every college teaching job I applied for prior, and subsequent, to going abroad was met with rejection. There were plenty, too. This was a bummer.

From one-year instructorships at large universities to entry level positions in small colleges, the result could be summed up thusly: No.

Some schools did not bother to answer. In looking for the slightest ray of hope, I interpreted this as a good sign. Maybe they still were deliberating. Yeah, right.

So much for the MFA from the University of Iowa Writers Workshop, ranked No. 1 in the field.

A terminal degree? Apparently, it was not a buyer's market for creative writing teachers or, for that matter, creative writers. Creative twittering, perhaps. Creative writing more than 140 characters, not so much.

Perhaps there's a paycheck in writing fake news. Maybe it was time to get started on The Great American Novel.

My old advisor, David James, told me to be patient. It takes time, he said.

For now, I needed a day job. Instead, I took a night job.

I became a bartender in Iowa City in the downtown Airport Bar & Grill, only a block off the campus and equidistant between two spots I frequented most as a grad student—the writer's workshop building and university library.

My apartment already was above the Airport. While cursing my unemployment status late one evening over a fourth Amstel, Rick, the bar's owner, offered work.

"Look, Flip, this is a natural," he said. "You're a good guy, funny, and probably would bring in some customers. I'm your landlord anyway since I own the building. Get behind in rent and I'll know where to find you."

The Airport was undeniably the community's best-known, casual watering hole, where town and gown freely mixed. And now, I would pour drinks for this crowd.

A deal was reached. I would have to give only a day's notice to quit if a college teaching job suddenly materialized. I got a nice discount on food and beer (not hard stuff or wine). Rick would deduct rent directly from my paycheck.

Also, as a MFA-certified, but unemployed, creative writer, Rick added this to my responsibilities: I would handle all future newspaper advertising copy and administer the Airport's Facebook and Twitter accounts announcing daily specials.

Hey, did that make me a professional writer?

11

Real life

SO, FLIP, YOU'RE going to be a bartender in the Airport Bar & Grill in downtown Iowa City. This took a while to get my arms around it. Could be worse, I guess.

What did I know about mixing drinks? At least this was a beer-drinking establishment in a college town. And, I did know the difference between red and white wine.

With my home above the bar for my two years in the MFA program, at least commuting to my new job would be a snap.

It would not require two bus trips and a ferry boat like it did in China. Maybe we could drill a big hole in my floor and I could slide down a pole like a fireman.

The job also meant I wouldn't be kept awake by noise from the bar trying to sleep above it. Now I contributed to that noise.

Furthermore, my schedule—late afternoons, nights, and two days off—gave me time to do some enterprise writing. On that front, there was modest success.

A satirical essay got published in Op-Ed section of the New York Times. A short story also got published in an academic anthology, which, while that meant few readers, looked good on the resume.

Nothing impresses academics like scarcely-read writing and research.

I talked my way into doing a weekly, freebie column on books for the local Gannett newspaper, the Iowa City Sentinel. This was expedited by the fact the editor was an Airport regular and, for sure, that the bar was a big advertiser.

This meant I could hang out with, and interview, authors who came to town for readings and to peddle their books. It also meant that the Sentinel could fill space with local content without giving benefits to the writer.

Hey, W.P. Kinsella found inspiration living here. He wrote the best-seller "*The Iowa Baseball Confederacy*" *and* "*Shoeless Joe*," which became the film "Field of Dreams."

That was the goal of everyone I knew in school: Write a book that gets made into a movie.

The writer's workshop had many distinguished teachers and alums over the years. Undoubtedly, they hung out in the Airport—and so I had that going for me: Two degrees of separation?

My adviser, David James, tossed part-time teaching, lecturing, and paper-grading crumbs my way. These included occasional short courses in the university's non-credit, community outreach writing program.

While regular faculty generally thought this was one step above mowing lawns and washing cars, I found it refreshing. These were people eager to tell stories needing more characters than could fit in a Tweet.

"Something will fall your way, Flip," David kept saying. "Just stick to it. You're young, single, no attachments. There could be worse situations. You could be a theatre major looking for work."

To be a good writer, in my mind two things were essential. You should be a good reader and a good observer of the human condition. Tending bar took care of the second ingredient.

The Airport was a never-ending assembly line of goofs, geniuses, eccentrics, culture clash, politics, war stories, clichés, celebrations, pickup lines and, oh yes, students. I kept notes.

Occasionally, the scene could get heated and blows were struck, though nothing would equal, Rick noted, the scuffles that occurred during the 2016 election campaign.

Typically, any fisticuffs came Saturdays in football season. We always were packed. Beers flowed like a coursing river. Almost always, you could figure trouble if someone wandered in wearing the colors of the visiting team and Iowa lost.

When he hired me, Rick said this: "Look at the football schedule and circle the dates for home games. Never ask to be off those days."

Thankfully, he always followed with this: "I'll pay overtime."

I was not expected to be a bouncer per se. My job, as an arbiter (referee?) for fights, was to first yell, "Take it outside, guys." I used to say "boys," but one time we had two young women in a fight.

If more encouragement was needed to restore order, Rick had a fool-proof "fight exterminator" hidden under the bar.

This was a very loud, piercing air horn, the kind used on yachts and large motorboats. The bartender blasted until he got everyone's attention. Then, he would pick up the other weapon—a bullhorn—and say, "Take it outside, guys."

While there wasn't much to be learned about the human condition when the bar was packed on weekends, the weekday afternoons offered an eclectic mix of slower-paced patrons with stories to tell.

This is when clientele ranged from students and professors to local businessmen. You always could count on a few retired townies, tired of staying cooped up inside and eager to eavesdrop for their entertainment.

Things were quieter then, and patrons generally came in looking for a conversation. If we weren't busy, I was the closest ear.

Many customers were celebrating, too. This could be for sports victories, passing a course or a test, end of an academic term, graduations and, on at least three occasions, boyfriends learning girlfriends were not pregnant.

We also were an easy walk from the county courthouse, which meant a steady trickle of lawyers, court clerks, and, in some memorable instances, exonerated defendants ready to buy "a round for the house."

The young defense lawyers fresh from law school were my favorites. Generally, they caught the gritty cases when defendants could not pay for counsel. They became the court-appointed attorney serving as temporary public defenders.

The pay for these gigs barely surpassed minimum wage, but the charges—dealing drugs, rape, assault, drunken driving, hate crimes—generally drew attention from news media. Me, too.

"Law school doesn't prepare you for some of the stuff you face," explained Jeff Richards, one of the lawyers who liked to linger in the Airliner. "I mean there are some real low life's out there, Flip. Stupid, too."

After a few beers got him loose, Jeff always had good tales about his more colorful cases. His favorite was defending the drunk driver who tried to escape cops on foot.

"At least this client was creative," said Jeff. "The guy had two previous DUIs. One night he plowed into a parked car on his way home from a tavern after closing-time. It was Christmas and the streets were slick. But what the hell, he was driving with a suspended license."

The police were there minutes later, he continued. In the process of giving him a sobriety test, and having him try to walk a straight line, the guy bolted. He knew he was looking at jail time, or at least loss of his license for good.

"So, he pushed one cop into the other," said Jeff, "and started running through yards and alleys. The police lost him, too. He might've got away, except this one cop heard a sneeze as he was returning to his car.

"The noise came from this big, life-sized nativity scene in front of a church. See, the guy was on his knees and hiding in the manger and posing as someone admiring the Baby Jesus.

"He was trying to be a fourth Wise Man, I guess."

You couldn't make up this stuff. Jeff and I became pretty good buddies. I told him if someday he didn't put his stories in a book, I was going to do it.

12

The plan

As BILLY "JACK" Burns cruised U.S. Highway 287 in Oklahoma at a very relaxed 87 mph after the interview, his first telephone call from his BMW z4 convertible—a wedding gift from the in-laws—was not to his bride of eight months, Merrilou.

Undoubtedly, she was playing tennis at the club.

"Jimmy!! I got it. We're in. They offered me the head coaching job. It's a done deal. Oh, I'm gonna make 'em wait a day before I say yes. We're not going to get rich, but it's another step closer. I can work stuff with the budget."

William Jackson Burns—on his birth certificate—was going places.

For now, this meant coaching basketball for a small college, Mesquite, in the most barren, godforsaken part of Oklahoma—the Panhandle. This was part of a plan.

Tomorrow? Madison Square Garden? Pauley Pavilion? The Palestra? Rupp Arena? In his book, the sky was the limit.

Billy Jack—to those who knew him best—had goals and he had a timetable. He wanted to be head coach in a major college basketball program by the time he was 32 years old. He had a little less than three to go.

He was hungry, ambition oozed from his pores. He studied and memorized playbooks and strategies of the masters—UCLA's John

Wooden, North Carolina's Dean Smith, and his personal favorites, Kentucky's John Calipari, Louisville's Rick Pitino and West Virginia's Bob Huggins.

"If you look and act like a successful basketball coach, you'll be a successful basketball coach," he liked to tell Merrilou, never one to argue that philosophy.

She was a full-fledged product of Houston's 1% scene with a clothes closet to prove it. Whenever queried, she explained her upbringing quite simply: "Daddy's in energy."

Her six-figure debutante party at the River Woods Country Club, with Willie Nelson—live—as entertainment, was the stuff of legends.

Billy Jack, too, took note of wardrobes and hairstyles. He leaned toward clothes favored by college basketball's coaching glitterati. His mostly off-the-rack closet could not match his bride's, but he was gaining.

Billy Jack personally attended five NCAA Final Four tournaments, but not to watch the games. Hell, he could do that on TV and learn more than sitting in the rafters of some domed arena.

No, the Final Fours also were coaching conventions to be mined and networked. He loved hanging out in hotel lobbies to note, and study, those who held the jobs he coveted.

Never mind that he stayed then in Motel 8s on the outskirts of the tournament cities. The idea was to look and act as if you *belonged*.

Once, he casually—but strategically—worked his way into a hotel bar conversation that included North Carolina's Roy Williams, Kansas's Bill Self, and TV announcer Dick Vitale.

He even drew a chuckle from this august gathering with his single contribution—wiped out, he felt, when Vitale slapped him on the back and responded with: "Good one, Bob."

Bob?

Well, moments like that soon would be history.

Now he was about to enter the next phase of his master plan: Head coach at a small college, or NCAA Division III, as it was formally known. In his mind, this would be a short stay.

13

On the move

THE MESQUITE COLLEGE job would be a calculated risk, Billy Jack reasoned. Peanuts in the big picture, but necessary.

It was rare, Billy Jack knew, someone from the small college ranks made the leap directly to a head coaching position at the major college level.

This would be similar to managing a corner convenience store en route to taking over a Costco. It did happen, though, and he had supreme confidence in his ability to make a name for himself in this fashion.

In his mind, it was risky to stay in any spot too long. There were too many examples of assistants in major college programs languishing on a bench, holding a clipboard, jockeying for a spot not far from the head guy, longing for face time on TV, and applying for every available job.

Billy Jack knew of one such assistant who totally destroyed a career in that role. It took one misstep. Literally.

This occurred during a nationally televised game, when the Kentucky assistant—at the far end of the bench— rushed to the team's huddle after timeout was called to gain a spot in the inner circle. Nothing looked worse for an ambitious assistant than being on the huddle's perimeter, straining to hear what the boss told the troops.

In his haste, he tripped. He landed face first on the floor, and his clipboard slid all the way past the court's center jump circle. Worse, a referee patted him on the butt after retrieving the clipboard for him.

His future would have surely escaped that, but the entire, embarrassing sequence got captured on film and became No. 5 on ESPN's weekly Top 10 highlight show on the subsequent weekend.

When the network aired its Top 10 highlights for the month later in December, his stumble inexplicably climbed to No. 3. And, worse, he was identified by name!

No athletic director was going to hand the reins of his or her basketball program to "the clown who fell on his ass on TV" as he became known.

Nope. Time to get some experience as the head guy, no matter what level of competition, before something stupid happened.

Besides, Billy Jack already had been an assistant immediately after his playing days at little Furlow College in Louisville.

This was a small school he carefully picked, first and foremost, because he knew he was good enough to play there. He was a point guard and starter for two of his four years for the Golden Eagles.

"Scrappy and smart," was his coach's description in Furlow athletic materials. He also was a team captain the last season, a credential that likely would gain entry for him into his alma mater's modest athletic hall of fame.

Big deal.

Billy Jack also had another important reason why he liked Furlow. It was blocks from the University of Louisville. He spent more time watching the Cardinals practice and play games than he invested as a player for his own school.

Certainly more time than he ever spent in a library.

Very early, Billy Jack was formulating his plan. Furlow was the launch pad. After graduating, he landed an assistant's job with Northern Michigan University, a NCAA Division II school.

He damned near froze his ass off that winter. He actually bought a pair of snowshoes—long discarded—that he used on several recruiting calls. He kept his fur cap with the big ear flaps "to remind me I paid my dues in the bush leagues."

Then, there came another D2 school: The University of West Florida on the Gulf Coast, where the smell of the BP oil spill still lingered, damage from Hurricane Katrina remained visible, and heat and humidity could suffocate an elephant.

Oh, and there was the constant roar of jets from a nearby U.S. Navy air station. He did learn to water ski, however. He still had the skis.

Finally, he moved up with an assistant's job in NCAA Division I—Eastern Kentucky University. Not exactly big time, but the travel budget was larger than that of Northern Michigan and West Florida combined.

Billy Jack was getting closer to his goal.

All he needed now was Southern Methodist on his resume and he would have all four directions covered—schools named Northern, Western, Eastern, and Southern.

Billy Jack was an Eastern Kentucky assistant only one year (a 15-16 record). A week away from a second season, he quit—totally pissing off the head coach—to spend two glorious years at a big-time, prestigious program in the Southeastern Conference.

A friend of a friend—who could keep track at this point?—set up the position.

Officially, he was a graduate student. That allowed him to become a grad assistant coach. It was an unpaid position, but he did receive a scholarship that helped with expenses. Never mind his undergraduate GPA was barely above the Mendoza line of 2.00.

Mostly he drove recruits back and forth from the airport, made sure players attended study halls, sat in on several recruiting visits (with strict orders to keep his mouth shut), and broke down game film of weaker, nonconference opponents.

Occasionally, he was assigned guard duty—made sure no underage players were in bars and in possession of fake IDs. Every morning started with scanning the police blotter report published in the local newspaper to note any arrests of players.

He *never* was asked for—nor volunteered—an opinion about strategy concerning a basketball game by those ahead of him on the coaching food chain. He was to be seen, not heard.

Billy walked a tightrope and he knew it. Any NCAA violations and he'd take the fall. That was a given.

While assistants served as buffers between head coaches and official NCAA transgressions, as a grad assistant he was on the real front lines. He was the very thin layer between bona fide, paid assistants and the dirty deeds themselves—whether or not he took part.

In just about any other profession, he would be called a bagman.

Those were unwritten rules. Billy Jack learned a lot. He was a sponge.

"Officially, I got a master's degree in 'Health & Recreation,'" he once joked to Merrilou, hot stuff as a cheerleader for the school during his stay. "But I got my PhD in how to run a basketball program."

Billy first made eye contact with his future bride during a game early in his first season, one of the few times he was allowed to sit on the bench with regular assistants.

Cheerleaders were a huge deal at this university. Hey, they won more national championships than the men's basketball program and that's saying a lot.

Merrilou figured any white male important enough to sit on the bench of her top-ranked team was a catch. Furthermore, he was a snappy dresser. His suit and tie—by design—was almost, but not quite, better than the head coach's.

After bumping into each other 2-3 times in student hangouts and a few outings, it was not long before Billy saw a new version of how she liked to do splits—naked and on her back—in his apartment.

"Keep moving, Merrilou, keep moving. That's reeeal good."

Gone, not forgotten

MY PERIODIC TEACHING gigs at Iowa were enjoyable, especially the workshop's short, non-credit courses for wannabe writers. These opportunities allowed me to massage my classroom techniques in case a job finally fell my way.

The classes were filled with a never-ending lineup of people wanting to do a memoir, but at best had enough in them for maybe 1-2 chapters. Most had no idea writing is mostly a boring, solitary exercise. Fattening, too, if there was a refrigerator in the vicinity.

Occasionally students did have good stories. I'll never forget my workshop on "developing a novel's characters."

So how do you think like a murderer, I asked a room full of students, if you've never killed anyone and you're writing a crime novel? Because, let's face it, no one in this class ever killed anyone. Right?

I looked around the room, just for effect, and during that slight pause a hand slowly raised in the front. Everyone froze.

Errr, care to tell us the circumstances, I asked—very politely, of course.

Turned out this man was a Vietnam War veteran. He was involved in the mortaring of a village his Army platoon was led to believe—mistakenly—was full of Viet Cong. It was not.

Among several dozen deaths were children, he told us, and their battered bodies and frightened, frozen expressions on their dead faces continued to haunt him.

Fifty years later, this class, he said, was the first time he acknowledged the incident and guilt it meant for him. He thought about the dead kids every day. Then, covering his face with his hands, he started sobbing.

Whew. No one knew how to respond. No one breathed.

I called for a break. Ten minutes later when we re-assembled, he did not return—that day or for any remaining class.

Three days later, I spotted him in the Airport bar. He was sitting by himself quietly nursing a beer at the end of the bar.

We made eye-contact as I headed to the restroom. He was gone when I returned.

I'll always wonder what happened to him.

15

Employment lines

MIDWAY IN MY first winter at the Airport, I energized my job search. I fired off another round of queries and applications.

Hiring for the upcoming academic year usually takes place in January. This is convenient for those who land a position. Then they have time to look for something better.

If they find it, this leaves the original employer desperate. That also was one way for me to enter. I didn't care if it was through the back door. I'd come down the chimney, if that's what it took.

The Chronicle of Higher Learning classifieds and higheredjobs.com became regular reading. I drew the line at online-only and for-profit schools. I wanted a traditional academic gig—corduroy jackets, preferably with elbow patches; Mr. Chips and all that.

In reading the notices it was difficult finding a fit. Higher education's dirty little secret—in my brief experience—was that few students can write very well, long or short form. But I *wanted* to teach writing, whether it was basic composition, essays, or letters to parents.

Most jobs I pursued were listed simply under "English & Literature." Very few said anything about writing at the undergraduate level. Too pedestrian.

I wasn't greedy. If I had to, I'd show the little rascals how to write advertising copy. According to Rick, my Airport ads in the Iowa City Sentinel were drawing customers.

But the job rejections slowly piled up ... Kansas State, Calvin, Denison, Wisconsin-Milwaukee, Rollins, Oklahoma, Oberlin and two schools named Concordia in different states, Minnesota and Texas.

I was willing to serve in the trenches, meet the freshmen at the door and start molding minds. Got an "Intro" course no one wants to teach? Call me.

I got plenty of advice from my sage adviser, David.

"The deal is this with college faculties," he said. "Get your foot in the door, put in a year or two kissing the dean's butt, and do not rock the boat at faculty meetings. Before long, you can organize and teach courses the way you want.

"You can have students writing to your heart's content. Undoubtedly, it's good for them. The truth is, most profs don't like to teach writing. Simple: Too many papers to grade, unless they have a TA, which generally doesn't happen in small liberal arts schools.

"Just don't commit any felonies. Don't screw coeds, or whatever your preference. The school doesn't want to fire you. It's a pain. The hiring process is a pain. Lots of political correctness, paperwork, and all that mumbo jumbo involved.

"Money's tight, too. Colleges don't want to spend money on searches. They'd rather hang on to some mediocre mope. Or a faculty spouse who already lives in town. No moving expenses. Get tenure, then you're really home free. They'd need pictures of the felony."

Of course, there was a fallback position for me. A return to China was not out of the question.

Jing, some faculty teammates on the basketball team, and others in China stayed in touch. I probably would send Bunny a thank you gift at some point. An Airport Bar & Grill t-shirt?

While the U.S. search continued, I had no trouble staying busy.

One night after closing, Rick surprised me with this: "Want to play basketball for me, Flip? I know you were good enough at it to play at Wake Forest. I need someone."

Lake Forest, Rick, not Wake Forest.

"No matter, you had to be decent. My guys aren't."

Funny how this sport just would not go away.

Rick's bar, the Airport Nose Divers, was entered in the Iowa City men's YMCA adult league. This was competitive stuff. Ex-Big 10 stars and other local hot shots were on rosters. Several played in European pro leagues.

Supposedly the league was amateur but no doubt a few sponsors slipped money under the table to their best guys. In some parts of the country, they'd be called ringers.

Hefty wagers almost always were at stake. Lots of testosterone here, flying elbows, bragging rights and all that.

Since most teams were sponsored by bars, it was a big deal to display the championship trophy and get your picture in the Sentinel. The games drew crowds beyond friends and family.

Not exactly the Stanley Cup or Lombardi Trophy, but good for business.

So, we worked a deal: I'd take over the coaching role to be a player-coach. Since the league played on a night I worked, he'd count that—playing, coaching hoops instead of bartending—as part of my regular work week. He'd pay for a sub bartender on game nights.

Hey! Suddenly, I was a professional basketball player. I got paid to play, right? Somewhere out there, my old high school and college coaches had to be laughing.

Our perennial last-place Nose Divers had not won a game in five tries when I joined. I'm proud to say we finished 11-7, won five straight in one stretch, and narrowly missed the playoffs for the best finish in a decade.

Unlike China, I never tossed in a shot from more than 20 feet. Rick was thrilled. "You know, Flip, I hope you can do this again next year. Maybe you'll get a job teaching here at Iowa, or somewhere close."

There was no mention of a raise, but no complaints. Things were perking along nicely for me.

My book column for the Iowa City Sentinel was picking up steam, getting numerous hits online as well as drawing letters on the Your Voice page. (I swear I did not write them using a pseudonym.)

The editor made a pitch to the Gannett headquarters for it to be distributed to the company's other newspapers. No word on that. The column opened other doors.

The author signings I attended in the local book stores—remember this was a university town—introduced me to writers and, more important, their agents. I learned a lot about publishing and someday that might come in handy.

There was a never-ending line of published writers coming to town, too. I read somewhere 130 million books have been published, with most done in the last decade. Approximately 750,000 get published annually in the U.S.

The authors I met in Iowa City at the store, or on the telephone, were a colorful group and mostly B list. I interviewed everyone from sushi chefs and TV talking heads to second tier—but successful—mystery writers and ex-professional athletes.

I had scruples. I refused to interview authors of self-help and get-rich books, plus TV evangelists. Also, I refused to interview anyone who wrote of experiences working for Donald Trump.

Several professors in the MFA program at Iowa made pitches to me to plug their work, most of which was self-serving and boring. Take a number, guys. Where were you when I needed a better grade in your course?

While I did not get paid for the book column, the Sentinel editor—everyone called him Murphy—liked my stuff well enough to toss a few feature story assignments my way. These paid.

Furthermore, some of my pieces got distributed throughout the Gannett chain. The accountants loved it. I was considered freelance and they still didn't have to pay benefits.

Meanwhile, my rejections continued to trickle in … Luther, SUNY-Fredonia, Alma, Wayne State, Buena Vista, Wittenberg, and two schools named St. Mary's in different states—Minnesota and Maryland.

Kindred spirits

IT WAS DURING his graduate assistantship when Billy Jack met Jimmy Cowens, a city kid from Chicago, another fringe figure in college basketball. Jimmy tried to make it as a walk-on, got cut, and never left town. He was the team's student manager for two seasons.

If there was one thing a college basketball coach going places like Billy Jack needed, it was a trusty No. 2 guy. They bonded big time when their paths crossed at Hoops, a popular sports bar where Jimmy waited tables part-time.

Each shared eagerness to make basketball his life. They closed Hoops many nights together. It helped that Jimmy got a discount. These sessions got spent deep into basketball.

Mostly they discussed Xs and Os, eligibility rules, NCAA regulations, and recruiting techniques. There was relentless quizzing of each other with game-time hypotheticals.

Question: "OK, you have the ball, you're down two points, there are 7 seconds remaining and you have no timeouts to set up a play. How can you stop the clock?"

First answer: "Have a player fake an injury and timeout is called by a referee. That's too easy."

Follow-up question: Which of your players fakes the injury?

Follow-up answer: Well, since rules say he has to come out let's make him the shortest, poorest shooter on the floor.

Billy, several years older and with coaching experience, always knew any journey to the top required a trustworthy assistant. This was how the system worked. He was tired of playing that role himself.

And Jimmy, street smart and smooth, knew he needed to hitch himself to an upwardly mobile wagon to get to his promised-land. If he wanted career liftoff, this was how it worked.

There would be many beers and slices of pizza—preferably pepperoni, thin crust—before coming to an understanding that sealed the bond: Either one of them, they realized, would cheat like hell if they thought they could get away with it.

It never was said in so many words, of course. Nevertheless, this unspoken bond could not be stronger if it had been witnessed, and sealed by a Notary Public.

There was little they disagreed about—on or off the court.

Well, Billy Jack had a little trouble with Jimmy's taste in music and clothes, a bit too "inner city" for him. But he did not consider it the least bit cynical to realize this could be important *street cred* someday in recruiting.

"You two are just a couple of basketball junkies," Merrilou occasionally would chide Billy. "If Jimmy wasn't black, I'd figure you for brothers. Twins, even."

Little did she know, and little would she want to know, the next stop in her marriage train with Billy Jack (and Jimmy): Beaver Junction, Okla. (pop. 1,287), home of Mesquite College.

How remote was the school that offered a head coaching job?

Let's put it this way. Picture a map of Oklahoma and the state's long, narrow strip in the far northwest corner in the heart of Dust Bowl country. The Panhandle.

Now, consider this: Mesquite, or "Tumbleweed Tech" as it gets called by opponents as well as some of its alumni, is 165 miles *northwest* of Northwest Oklahoma State University.

On big, clear nights, the Moon appeared to be within an arm's reach whether or not it was full. In some directions, the horizon was a bleak, unblemished straight line without one tree or tall shrub to break the monotony.

Decades after the Great Depression, dangerous dust storms that blackened the skies still could present a driving hazard. They claimed 2-3 driving deaths annually.

Well, hell, that was fine with Billy.

He figured it this way. The more remote the school, the easier it would be to operate without scrutiny. You know, cheat. He'd build a powerhouse there in 2-3 years that won an NCAA small college championship before anyone noticed.

Then, with offers rolling in from major college programs looking for an energetic, young coach to turn around their program, he was gone. Then Jimmy would either inherit the Mesquite job from Billy or follow him to the next stop. What could go wrong?

If Mesquite got into NCAA trouble, so be it. No one kept score on coaches unless you did not win enough games. Just get out of Dodge before the sheriff arrived.

"What will Merrilou say about going to Mesquite?" asked Jimmy, finishing off their telephone call as Billy Jack flew down the highway in his BMW. "This ain't exactly her beloved Houston."

"She's excited for me to be a head coach somewhere. She just doesn't know where. Anyway, geography's not her strong suit."

"What is?"

"Her birthday suit, bro. Her birthday suit."

CHAPTER

17

Upwardly mobile

"YOU'RE GOING WHERE?

"Billy Jack's going to coach what? Mesquite College? Never heard of
it. In Beaver Junction?

"Honeyboo, that's the frickin' Panhandle. Hell, if the tornadoes and
dust storms don't getcha, the earthquakes will. That's friggin' frackin'
country, girl."

This was not the response Merrilou expected from her father, Harold
(Big Hal) Mason. She was seconds from getting off the telephone with
Billy Jack on his car phone.

Her immediate call to Big Hal was a natural, reflex action. She was
Daddy's girl and, as far as he was concerned, whatever Merrilou wanted
Merrilou got.

Willie Nelson for your coming out party? No problem, Honeyboo.
How about the Steve Miller Band for an opening act?

Billy Jack's glowing descriptions of Mesquite College, its Oklahoma
Panhandle location, made it sound as if their new home—their first,
considering they lived in her parents' guest house since the wedding—
was an ivy-covered seat of higher learning in a New England setting.
Just down the road from ski country in Taos in New Mexico.

Now Merrilou was confused. Big Hal wasn't.

Harold Mason was quite familiar with the Oklahoma Panhandle. That's where he got his start in oil as a wildcatter with, he fondly recalled, a little tomcatting on the side.

Beaver Junction? Been there. Guymon? Been there, too. Boise City? Ditto.

This was Oklahoma's armpit, as far as he was concerned. Hell, these were featured towns in that Ken Burns "Dust Bowl" documentary. Things had not changed that much, probably worse.

Truth be told, Big Hal didn't exactly strike it rich in the Panhandle. This remote corner of Oklahoma was one of several locations he drilled dry holes. He was one of the few to bust out. This did little to improve his fondness for that part of the country.

In fact, he was not a real oil man. He finally found success the old-fashioned way, relying on his wife Ruthie's family fortune. After the drilling flops, there came a stern lecture on economics from his now deceased father-in-law.

Then, this was followed by wisely investing in deals and partnerships with more knowledgeable oil men recommended by Ruthie's old man. These were harvested and cultivated in Houston's River Woods Country Club locker room, on the golf course, and at popular athletic events.

His run was spectacular. From oil, he shifted to natural gas at just the right time and, then, thanks to people like Ross Perot, got on the ground floor of technology. This included investments with Texas Instrument and Dell, plus startups that became household brands based in the Austin area.

Merrilou, an only child, worshipped her father. A long, previous string of boyfriends never got close to measuring up to him—"mutts" he called them when she wasn't in earshot.

Even though he was never much of an athlete and had a golf handicap pushing 20, Big Hal was a sports fan and knew its value. He still owned a small piece of the Tennessee Titans, dating to the NFL franchise's years in Houston.

He had skyboxes for all the major, local pro teams—Astros, Texans, and Rockets. He was two rows behind George Bush Sr. when Houston won the 2017 World Series. He always got access to a pal's box for the annual Texas-Oklahoma football game in Dallas. Cotton Bowl? No problem. Who's playing?

Big Hal was intrigued by Billy Jack.

He recognized the ambition and his overall "cut of the jib," seeing a little bit of himself in his daughter's latest derby entry. He knew nothing of college basketball, but, like the good money man he was, he would not mind investing in his son-in-law's future.

Hell, it might be kind of fun to go to one of those Final Four's, or whatever they're called. Maybe good for business, too.

18

Mud in your eye

BILLY JACK WOULD need real basketball players to come to Mesquite. Meanwhile, there was no question about the importance of his first recruit: Merrilou.

He needed to sell her on Beaver Junction. This would not be easy.

For starters, he had to get past the word "Beaver." Damn, couldn't the town be named something different?

Everywhere he turned it was Beaver this and Beaver that—seat of government for Beaver County with the nearby Beaver River running through the Beaver State Park and creating the Beaver Dunes with the aid of Beaver Dam.

Embarrassing!

Thank God it was Mesquite College, and the sports teams were at least called the Buckaroos. He couldn't imagine what opposing crowds would chant if they were the Mesquite Beavers. Or, worse, if it were called Beaver College Beavers.

He plotted and planned Merrilou's first visit to Beaver Junction as if it were the Normandy invasion. Jimmy tried to help, but, as someone raised in inner-city Chicago, his suggestions were, well, worthless.

Most likely he still was in shock himself from his own first visit.

"Jimmy, you got to understand. You can't walk down to the corner bodega and buy a pint. You can't even walk down to the corner and buy milk, for that matter."

How small was Beaver Junction? Billy Jack was told by a woman in the post office that the first baby of the New Year sometimes didn't arrive until March.

There was a town square with the Beaver County courthouse in the middle. Most of the business fronts had "for lease" and "for sale" signs in the window. Several had been re-purposed into apartments.

The only downtown businesses were a post office, convenience store, tanning salon, video rental shop, three taverns on opposite sides of the square, barber shop, Mobil station at one corner, Amy's flower shop, and a restaurant called, yep, the Beaver Café.

God only knew where students went for fun. For sure, it wasn't here.

The movie theatre was boarded up long ago. Several letters were missing, but the marquee showed the final film shown was "The Last Picture Show." Had to be somebody's joke, right?

A block off the square was, natch, the Beaver County History Museum, which was next door to the Beaver County Library. It was an original Carnegie library, and looked as if nothing had been done to keep it structurally safe for decades.

There was a cluster of commerce on the highway on the town's edge: Another gas station with a convenience store, John Deere dealership, used car lot, Dollar General store, Beaver Motel, and entrance to the Beaver County Fairgrounds.

Billy Jack had no idea what, if anything, would appeal to Merrilou.

He was counting on the college itself, which, with an enrollment of about 950 students, was comprised of eight, faded-brick buildings within a short walk of the town square. This was not counting the three portable classroom trailers.

This was not an ivy-covered institution in a New England setting.

She was passionate about tennis and hopefully someone in town shared her interest. On the other hand, the only court he found to show her, and then decided not to, had grass—weeds, really—growing in cracks that splintered the playing surface.

There was a golf course, but it hardly was a country club. A trailer passed for a pro shop. The only other building was a shed that housed riding lawnmowers. There was no practice range.

There were only nine holes and five scrubby trees on the entire, flat layout. There were no sand traps, but plenty of sand in the middle of the fairways.

The biggest hazards, Billy Jack learned the few times he played Beaver (naturally) Golf Club, were the dust storms that blew in from surrounding flat prairies.

It was as easy to see your ball disappear into a gopher hole on the fairway as it was to see it roll into the cup. Once, he found a rattlesnake wrapped around his ball. He took a free drop. No one in his group argued.

Where would they live? The school had staff apartments available. These had approximately the same square footage as his new bride's bedroom clothes closet in Houston.

Billy Jack never gave Mesquite's housing a chance. No way it'd ring Merrilou's bell, but maybe something would be suitable for Jimmy.

There always was the possibility of renting something in town, too. Well, on second thought, maybe not.

Merrilou's initial cheerfulness, fueled by Billy Jack's almost-over-the-top enthusiasm, waned with every corner they turned in Beaver Junction.

As she took in what could be her home town for the next few years, her smiles got tighter, more forced. A worry line crossed her brow.

This was a new world for her, a product of Houston's best social circles. Her idea of roughing it was using a tennis racket with a loose string.

This was another planet, where Pesto Shrimp and Chocolate Truffle layer cake lunches at the club gave way to corn dogs and pop tarts on a picnic table.

Merrilou's beloved, serious yoga lessons and a continuance thereof definitely were out, of course. Hey, maybe she could introduce yoga to the locals and teach a class?

Might be worth asking, set up a studio in one of those vacant buildings on the square. Yeah, right.

Billy Jack was put to the ultimate test of salesmanship.

Before they checked into the Beaver Motel (fill in your own punch line on that), he made one spontaneous, final stop that possibly would soften his young wife.

"The county fair's going on this week," he said. "It's right across the street from the motel. What do you say we stop and browse? Get a closer look at things. Maybe meet some locals. Might be a hoot, fun."

Merrilou perked up a bit as they browsed tents. The exhibits featured crafts, paintings, canned fruits, homemade pies, and other foods. People were friendly, too.

Though a city girl, this was a bit like the open-air markets she'd shopped on Spain's Costa del Sol while spending vacations in the family villa—IF you had a healthy imagination. Even the smaller livestock and pets made her smile.

Then, some loud cheering from a grandstand across the fairgrounds caught their attention.

"Let's go see what all the noise is about," said Billy Jack, a decision he would regret. "Maybe it's some sort of competition."

It was exactly that.

They took seats in the stands and, on a dirt, oval track used for stock car racing, watched men carrying a brown, disc-like object dash 25 yards or so to a chalked line. There, they would fling the brown disc with a mighty heave. Then, the distances were measured solemnly by a referee in a black-and-white striped shirt.

Merrilou, turning around, asked a local in a cowboy hat and boots—with spurs, no less—sitting behind them: What are the objects being thrown?

"They look sort of like a Frisbee, or one of those things—a discus—they throw at track meets," she added. "It looks like fun."

"They're cow chips, Ma'am," he said.

"Cow chips? What are cow chips?"

"You know. Cow poop, to be polite. Some call them cow pies. Either way, it's dried and hard. Petrified poop, like a rock. This here's the annual world cow-chip throwing championship. Winner gets a big trophy and braggin' rights for a year."

"Oh."

For nearly a minute, Merrilou and Billy Jack were silent, stared straight ahead, their brains processing what they just heard, but avoiding eye contact.

For certain, this sealed the deal.

He knew there was no way in hell his new bride would be living in Beaver Junction, home of the world championship cow chip throwing contest.

If word got out to her Houston pals, she'd be a laughing stock. They politely excused themselves, and headed for the exit aisle and their motel.

The local in the cowboy gear called out behind them: "You're going to miss the ladies' division if you leave now. If you want, it's probably not too late to register and compete."

19

Now what?

THERE WAS AN early-morning checkout from the Beaver Motel for the young Burns' couple following that first, full day together in Beaver Junction. There would not be a second day.

Uncharacteristically, Billy Jack was in full retreat. He needed to re-group. In a hurry. This meant no lunch in the student union, visit to the field house, chat with the provost, or peek at the basketball office. Maybe it was just as well. It could only get worse.

Confident that Mesquite still was the right place for him to coach, if not live, adjustments definitely were in order for his wife. He prided himself on his ability to read people and make adjustments.

Merrilou made that obvious when they retired early to bed that first—and only—night of the visit. She pulled the covers tightly around her, and turned her back to him. There was no arguing, just borderline sulking. They weren't married long enough for a genuine argument.

His mind churned. Sleep did not come easy.

As the Mesquite College coach, he knew he'd be on the road most of the time. Merrilou told him she was resigned to this, and was braced for lengthy separations.

This was a price to be paid to get to the big time. She was aware. Secretly, she wanted the big time for herself as much as for him.

But, hey, she needed her creature comforts. Live in the "Cow Chip Capitol" of the world? No way, big boy. They needed to find middle ground.

After pulling from the motel parking lot, he aimed his car straight for Texas and Amarillo—with Billy Jack in serious need of a Plan B.

The return trip to the airport in the rental car was a little over 120 miles. Amarillo (pop. 196,000) was the nearest city of consequence to Beaver Junction.

There was nothing but prairie to see out the windows as they zipped down U.S. Highway 287. Both were deep into thought. The bleak, long drive made the stalemate seem more desperate. Little was said.

Merrilou did not wish to remain in Houston while her husband coached more than 800 miles away in another state. This simply did not look good.

Would she attend everything in Houston—parties, celebrations, weddings, reunions, receptions, reunions—by herself?

Her husband, in the hoopla that surrounded their wedding at the country club, impressed everyone as someone going places. Handsome, too. A good catch for Merrilou, they said.

Fine, but where *was* he? How could she explain his many absences and her solo appearances at events around town? To her friends, she'd look like some sort of loser, a lonely and forgotten ornament.

Pssst. Were they already having trouble? Told you this wouldn't work. She could hear it all now.

Worse, she'd be a captive audience for her parents if she continued to live alone most of the time in the family guest house.

Yikes! The last thing she wanted was attempts by Big Hal and Ruthie to make her part of *their* social life.

She was totally confident there was no risk Billy Jack, ahem, would stray with so many nights elsewhere. In Beaver Junction? No way.

A few surprise visits could take care of that. She'd pack her cheerleader outfit. Billy loved watching her private routines just for him, which typically ended with her in nothing but sweat socks and sneakers.

When they reached the Amarillo airport in what had been almost total silence, neither had a solution to housing. Then, things seemingly went from bad to worse.

They were a day early. The return tickets were for the next day. In all the anxiety, he had not called ahead to make a change.

The connections to Houston were full, unless they wanted to fly by way of Denver with a long layover in Colorado. They'd have to spend the night in Amarillo.

Little did they know, this was a good thing.

20

China syndrome

NO JOKE: SO these three Chinese customers, two men, one woman, walked into the Airport Bar & Grill one day. They sat at a table. They appeared to be a wee bit shy.

So I walked over and said: *Wǒ néng bāng nǐ shénme ma? Píjiǔ*?

They were startled, which startled me.

It was startling because, in what had to be my lame attempt at the Chinese language, they actually understood me: What can I do for you? Beer?

See, important stuff, like Píjiǔ, which means beer, I still remembered.

They were disappointed we had no Tsingtao or Yanjing, two of China's more popular beers. I told them we ran out yesterday and awaited a fresh delivery. The trio ordered Heinekens.

It was obvious they appreciated my effort. Eventually, after a second round of drinks, they invited me to join them on my break. This would be fortunate.

They were with a Chinese film production company. Their names were Hu Jun ("call me Hugh"), Zhou Zivi ("I'm 'Ziv'"), and Maggie Wei (no problem here).

Traveling in the U.S. on a grant, they were in an exchange program to visit university cinema departments. Their Iowa City stop just began and would go another two weeks.

"This has been a very enlightening trip so far," explained Maggie. "We visited the University of Illinois before here. We wanted to see where Ang Lee went to school.

"Next we go to New York University. Then, we visit the University of Southern California and then return to Shanghai."

Lee was the Oscar-winning director from Taiwan of "Crouching Tiger, Hidden Dragon" and later "Life of Pi." His work was part of an explosion of interest in Chinese filmmaking, which sees about 20 or so new screens per day opening to the public.

We're way beyond Jackie Chan here, folks.

My new friends were ecstatic to learn of my Xiamen University visit. Maggie calculated she was on the campus for a visit when I was teaching there, though pretty sure she never saw me play basketball on my faculty team.

Small world, China. Well, not really.

When I told them of my experience showing "China Syndrome" to my classes, their interest perked up more. They were especially interested in the students' reactions.

"We are very interested in learning common grounds on this trip," said Hu. "What films and stories have cross-cultural appeal. We make hundreds of films every year in China."

My new friends went on to explain the growing trend in Chinese films: "Little Fresh Meat," or films with young, fresh-looking stars.

Teenagers were a huge part of the ticket-buying market, but mostly they had no interest in stilted, propaganda-laden storylines. They associated young, new faces with this taste.

"This is what appeals to our growing market. How can we increase this? But how can we make films that also appeal in the West."

Sounded reasonable to me. The Airport chat could've continued into the night. I had to get back to my duties. We promised to meet again, which we did several times during their stay.

Meanwhile, with the traditional hiring window for the next academic year starting to close, my number of application rejections also was enlarging … Colorado State, Hope (which I was losing), DePaul, Bowling Green, Knox, and two schools named Wesleyan in different states—Nebraska and Ohio.

CHAPTER

21

Write stuff

LATE ONE MORNING, my telephone rang. It was Murphy from the Sentinel.

"Look, Flip, I got a problem. The new feature writer I hired needs to delay her start date. Can you pump out some pieces for me to cover her ass? You got a nice touch, and take your pick. I got a short list of 6-7 things I could use, you pick three."

If done right, feature stories are not as easy as Murph, a typical editor, makes it sound. You don't simply push a button and words spill out. Editors were failed writers, after all.

The extra money, let alone the exposure, would be nice. I didn't want to turn down the assignments, but the basketball season was over. I was back to working five nights at the bar.

I'd need some no-brainers on the list, quick profiles of local celebs, charities, etc. That kind of stuff. One thing for sure. There never was a shortage of people, or groups, wanting to see their name in print.

I could devote some daytime hours, plus the two days I did not bartend, to the task. I'd do some of the spadework on the telephone. We negotiated deadlines.

We quickly settled on two feature articles. One would be a 100th birthday celebration for a retired farmer, and World War II veteran, living in a local assisted care facility. Putty in my hands.

The other on a local high school football star just discharged from the military after two tours in Iraq. "Stay away from politics," said Murphy. "That's all I ask on that one."

The third?

This was my own idea, and took some selling. Why not a piece about the visiting Chinese film group?

"Nobody gives a shit, Flip. I mean what does that have to do with our local readers. Think local here."

This became a tug-of-war.

The university, like many U.S. college towns, had many significant resources—cultural, business, political, charitable, educational, scientific—to offer the town.

Interesting and significant people, like my new Chinese pals, came through all the time.

But unless they played football or basketball for the university, few locals outside the school took advantage of the offerings. Maybe attending an occasional theatre production—typically a touring Broadway performance by a B-list company—was an exception.

"Look at the big picture here, Murph. They may not be local, but everyone likes movies. These guys produce them. I can make it interesting, trust me.

"I'll work in lots of local color, talk to the university people here involved. They're subscribers, too. I'll even work in managers of the local movie theatres. They're advertisers, don't forget."

That last pitch—advertising—did it, of course.

Murphy gave a reluctant OK on the third feature article. This gave me a chance to spend more time with the Chinese visitors, an interesting group.

But the big winner, ironically, turned out to be my editor. The story went national.

When the Gannett bosses at the Virginia headquarters saw it on the projected news budgets from the satellites, they grabbed it for distribution to their hundred or so newspapers. It became a page one piece for its USA Today feature section.

Murphy, of course, became a hero in the big bosses' eyes.

"You think there's a follow-up here," he said, in his call to tell me about the story's future. "I mean these guys are big in China. I had no idea."

"Not unless you want to expense me to China, big guy. They're gone, left town two days ago."

And my real future? The hiring window was shut with final rejections from New Mexico Highlands, Transylvania, Puget Sound, St. Olaf, and schools named Trinity in different states—Connecticut and Texas. Unless something changed, I was another year away from a college teaching job.

22

Home sweet home

TO MOST VISITORS, Amarillo is simply a large city in Texas halfway between Oklahoma City and Albuquerque on Interstate 40. There's not much but barren, windswept prairie and abandoned oil wells separating these three cities.

Mostly tourists keep driving through, or stop very briefly, in Amarillo. They hurry to put this part of the country in their rearview mirror. They are snowbirds escaping cold, Upper Midwest winters and headed to Arizona.

Amarillo is the city many tourists know to be the home of the Texas Steak Ranch, which, according to miles and miles of advance, over-the-top billboard advertising, offers a 72-ounce slab of meat.

Eat it in an hour and it's free. Participants do not have to be accompanied by an adult. A nurse might be a good idea, though.

See, this is cowboy country. Cattle processing remains important to the local economy. If the breeze blows in the right direction, this becomes very evident to visitors.

Some say the city's most famous native was "Amarillo Slim" Preston, early star on the Las Vegas poker circuit. Others vote for businessman T. Boone Pickens.

There is a long strip on I-40 through Amarillo loaded with the usual franchises—motels, restaurants, service stations, muffler shops—to accommodate visitors. One guide lists Cracker Barrel among the top places to dine, just a few notches below Texas Steak Ranch.

Travelers rarely stray far from the interstate highway. Billy Jack, trying to salvage something on the dreary and tense drive from Oklahoma, decided to look for something better than Holiday Inn Express or Best Western for the unscheduled, overnight stay.

He found it. In fact, it was hard to miss. At 12 stories high, the Marriott in the downtown commercial section was one of the tallest buildings in five counties.

The former home of the Cattlemen's Hotel, it had been remodeled, modernized, and, as Merrilou noted, was quite plush. Bell boys and excellent restaurant, too. This was not the Beaver Motel.

After freshening up, Billy Jack and Merrilou went for a drive and continued to be pleasantly surprised.

Their discoveries included several public golf courses, a tony-looking country club, gated estates, green parks, zoo, glass and steel civic center, and huge fairgrounds, which, as far as they could see, did not host cow chip tossing contests.

There also was a stylish, new performing arts center. Merrilou made Billy Jack stop here, jumped out of the car, and went to the ticket booth, where she learned of an upcoming Pink Martini concert she'd actually like to attend.

There also was a community playhouse not far away, which they learned occasionally hosted road performances of Broadway productions. She wasn't big on theater but loved opening night parties.

They also stumbled upon two nice looking condominium developments with town homes, swimming pools, and tennis courts. It was here, at almost the same moment, light bulbs went off in their heads.

"Why not Amarillo?"

It was a two-hour or so drive from Beaver Junction, but so what?

Billy Jack would be on the road most of the time. If flying was involved, it would have to be from the airport in Amarillo anyway—the nearest with commercial flights.

He could keep a smaller place in Beaver Junction. Maybe rent what the college had to offer as a sort of crash pad for extended stays in Beaver Junction, where Merrilou could join him for short stays.

Too expensive?

Nothing was said, but they both knew Big Hal was good for whatever they needed. Nothing but the best for his Honeyboo.

Their night in Amarillo in the downtown Marriott became a most pleasant stay, even though she forgot to pack her cheerleader outfit for this trip.

23

Lights! Camera! Action!

FlipD @jing_chi 10 May 2019
You met Hu Jun? Wow!!..Saw story, awesome…what's he like? His
films are huge…big campus followings…..

MY STORY REACHED China? Jing's tweet alerted me.

After a few more exchanges, I learned she saw my piece on the USA Today web page. Also, it got reprinted by the South China Morning Post and two smaller, English-language Hong Kong newspapers.

Kind of mind-boggling to think my writing was read in China. This was big time for a writer. A billion people and, give or take, two billion eyeballs.

I did not doubt for a second the enterprising Jing found the USA Today page with ease. Unlike what Americans are led to believe, most Chinese have access to important international Internet news sites.

In my stay in Xiamen, I had no difficulty pulling up everything from the Los Angeles Times to Reuters. No censorship police came busting through my door. But to this day, I'll never quite understand how Jing had a Twitter account that reached me.

Social media that extended outside the country was, in many cases, limited. The Chinese, like other nations, grapple with technology and the communication industry. The leaders are aware of the potential, and try to keep a grip on flow of information.

In the last 60-70 years, the country's fought its way through, or simply survived, more purges, reforms, and political movements than a Central American banana republic.

The Chinese now are crazy for entertainment. In my Xiamen teaching stay, it was obvious students were transfixed by Western culture in general, pop culture in detail. Never a day passed in the classroom without someone wearing a t-shirt, or some article of clothing, devoted to it.

But nothing was moving faster than China's film industry. Government and business leaders, noting the unquenchable thirst for action on big and small screens, were—like capitalists everywhere—eager to cash.

"There is great potential in this industry in China," I recalled Hu Jun telling me in one of our Iowa City chats. "We think there is much we can learn from each other. I like to be part of this growth."

Potential? The largest movie studio in the world was now located in China, where the industry was a multibillion dollar enterprise. There are dozens of film companies, and thousands of movie houses.

A million or more Chinese make a living as actors, directors, production assistants, cameramen, publicists, etc. In particular, I also learned of *Xiao Xian Rou*—the craving among movie goers for handsome, young male stars.

Think Justin Bieber, I guess. This was new turf for me, and it made me feel very old.

"In English, this is translated to 'Little Fresh Meat,'" said Maggie Wei, in one conversation I had with the visiting Chinese. "Young women in our country are having much, new influence in our society. They spend money.

"Their idols, their dreams center on young, handsome teenaged males their age. We call this new wave of stars 'Little Fresh Meat.' The young girls go to the films that feature these young men.

"It is a way—a new way in China—for them to express their sexuality.

"Is it not this way in America?"

Hard to say no, but little did I know how big a part Hu, as a director-producer, played in this arena.

He was a star in what I later learned China calls its Sixth Generation of filmmakers. He had received numerous awards for his films both domestically and in international festivals from Venice to Toronto.

Hell, in his country he was Mike Nichols, Steven Spielberg, Ron Howard, etc. Take your pick. I should've asked for an autograph instead of an interview in our Iowa City chats.

Hollywood was another story for him. He was taking aim, though. His U.S. tour, and stop in the Midwest, was part of a strategy.

Tired of making popular films that did little to inform and educate Chinese audiences, he wanted to get deeper into documentaries and bridge gaps, break down walls between nations.

This could be tricky territory, he confided. Occasionally his government's censors could make things difficult, but there was no question the atmosphere was becoming more relaxed.

"I am in the world of poetry," he said. "I simply need to write the correct poems."

The Cultural Revolution got overtaken—trampled, really—by a Cultural Gold Rush.

24

A telephone call

IN LATE JULY on a hot, sweaty Saturday afternoon, I served drinks in the Airport to a table crammed with softball players. They played for Little Joe's Place, another Iowa City bar around the corner.

Rick loved it, of course. Here was a uniformed team from a competing bar sitting in his establishment merrily spending money and swilling away. This was better advertising than buying space on a highway billboard.

Little did anyone know, Rick offered all tavern-sponsored softball teams a group rate with one condition: Drinks were half-price if at least six came to the Airport and wore their uniforms.

Of course, little did Rick know that many players loaned their uniforms to friends and relatives to take advantage of the group rate. It's a dog-eat-dog world out there, folks.

I brought over several more pitchers of beer when my cell rang in my pocket.

You cannot miss it when I get a call. The ringtone is, well, distinctive: *Anchors Aweigh*. On several occasions, Navy vets who were customers popped to attention when it sounded.

I set it up that way in deference to a high school buddy who went to Annapolis and became a SEAL. A rumor, unconfirmed, was that he was on the team that snuffed out Osama bin Laden.

Usually I turn it off while working. It was not unusual for "buddies" to annoy me with a call from the other side of the bar to order more beer, cheese balls, or whatever. This was not the case with this call. Decidedly.

"Hello, is this Phillip Doyle?"

When someone starts a call using my full name, I brace myself. No one uses Phillip unless they are reading from a piece of paper.

Or, as it turned out this time, an application!! Bingo!! Voila!! Happy days are here again?

"Yes, well, this is Flip... I mean Phillip. I'm kind of in the middle of something here. How can I help you?"

"Oh, well, sorry. This is Jonathan Casey. I'm president of William Harrison College. I realize this may be, ah, a bit unusual to be calling like this on a Saturday. Can we schedule a time soon to talk when you're not so busy?"

William Harrison College. Harrison College. Harrison.

The president of the school? The school's president was calling me?

My brain exploded. Where the hell was Harrison? I'd applied to so many schools I'd lost track. Damn. Was it in Ohio? Pennsylvania? Missouri? Hopefully, not one of the Dakota's.

Then, from the other side of the room in a booming voice that could be heard as far away as the Dakota's (and certainly by my caller): "Hey, Flip. Where's my beer? I got two pitchers coming."

Next, of course, someone started playing music—loudly—on our big screen video to add more noise to the background. This was enough to turn any telephone conversation into a shouting match.

Then there was a huge roar as members of Bonehead's, another tavern softball team, crashed through the doors anxious to celebrate victory.

Good news for the Airport and Rick. Bad for me.

"My, it does sound like I caught you in the middle of something," said Casey, my caller. "Let's figure a time. I would like to have a chat."

Chat? Hell yes. For sure. Damn straight. Right on, Mr. President.

We agreed to the next afternoon. This would give me breathing room. I needed to reconnoiter.

Tippecanoe bound?

SO, WILLIAM HARRISON College in Indiana?

Later, I got on Google and dug deeper.

In far southern Indiana, equidistant between Evansville and Louisville, Ky.

In a county seat town called Harrison with a population of 11,392. And no major highways running through it.

Here was the thumbnail gathered from *Wikipedia* and additional sources:

William H. Harrison College is a private liberal arts college in Harrison, Ind., founded in 1846 by the Presbyterian Church of the USA. Originally named Tippecanoe College, it was re-named in 1861 to honor former United States President William H. Harrison. There are branch campuses in Evansville and Louisville, Ky.

Enrollment: 1,115

Acceptance rate: 59%

Graduation rate: 51%

Accreditation: NCA, IBE

Tuition: $32,000 per academic year (semesters)

Endowment: $40.2 million.

Mascot: Colonials.

Colors: Red, white, blue.
Notable alums: Wilma Crenshaw '72, Teacher of The Year (1984),
Indiana Education Association; Hon. James K. McCutcheon '48,
Deputy U.S. Ambassador to Belize (1972-74); Herman "Bud" Span-
gler '62, author, "Bass Fishing Made EZ"; Tom Duffy '70, president
(1998-2002), Muffler Manufacturers Association of America; Con-
nie Thompson '94, grand prize winner, "Price Is Right"; and
Millicent van Vlissingen '72, contemporary poet.

This was not Ivy League. Not even Junior Ivy. On the other hand, not exactly Poison Ivy.

At first blush, it appeared to be like hundreds of other perfectly fine, small liberal arts colleges in the U.S. not unlike the one where I got my undergraduate degree.

I read everything in preparation for the call from President Casey. The digging confirmed a fast-developing theory of mine.

Through keen observation, years of study (as I closed in on age 30), much research, and, of course, tending bar, it was: Real life is often stranger than fiction.

In this case, it was the school's namesake, William H. Harrison.

In 1841, Harrison became the oldest person then to be elected to the White House at age 67—and served exactly one month in office. Actually, much of that month was spent in bed and not in an office.

Old Willy, apparently to prove he was a vigorous chap despite his age, gave an inaugural speech from the U.S. Capitol steps on a cold, wet day in early March without an overcoat or hat.

Oh, and the speech was longest in U.S. history at 8,445 words. We're talking a short novel here. His address clocked at just over four hours. Hope nobody on the stage had to go to the bathroom.

Then, he declined riding in a covered carriage in the parade back to the White House down Pennsylvania Avenue, opting for his own horse. That night he tripped the light fantastic with his wife, Anna, attending three different inaugural balls.

This eventually led to what was diagnosed then as "pneumonia of the lower lobe of the right lung." There are differing opinions on this, given the Capitol was very close to germ-infested swamps and a then less-than-pristine Potomac River.

Anything was possible. Among medicines given to the fast-fading Harrison: Castor Oil, opium, leeches, and—I am not making this up—Virginia snakeweed. He died 31 days after the swearing-in ceremony.

That made U.S. President No. 9 more like 8½. Less, if you're good with fractions.

He was replaced by John Tyler. You know, "Tippecanoe and Tyler Too"? This was their slogan during the election campaign.

Tippecanoe was a reference to Harrison's military career. He was the general in charge of fighting Indians in what was then known as the Northwest Territories, and now Indiana and Ohio. His signature victory was "The Battle of Tippecanoe," fought in 1811 in Indiana.

No one was quite ready for Tyler as his successor. He became the first in-office VP in U.S. history to become president. This earned for him the nickname, "His Accidency."

John-boy managed to live down to expectations, too. Depending on whose list you consult, he can be found on the Top 5 list of "worst U.S. presidents" typically between Millard Fillmore and Warren Harding.

See what I mean about real life being more entertaining than fiction? As far as I could learn, this was the only traditional college named specifically for William H. Harrison.

There's always confusion about Harrison, however. His grandson, Benjamin, was elected U.S. president in 1889, made it through a full term and earned high marks.

The school rang a distant memory bell for me. I thumbed through my pile of rejections both on paper and online.

To be honest, I could not recall how or where I stumbled onto this job opening in the first place. I was looking at a slot in the English department, I guess. What did I say in my application?

There it was: Three months ago, in a letter signed by the school's dean of faculty, Dr. D. Nelson Brunk, I was turned down for whatever job I was seeking.

"… I regret to inform you that the position will not be available." No real explanation. Just hit the road, Jack.

Curious that now, after shown the door by a dean, the school president might be opening it. Or at least I assumed this was the case.

Our call was scheduled for 2 p.m. on Sunday, one of my off-days. I'd get answers soon enough.

26

Home sweet homes

THE OPENING OF a new Mesquite school year, the first for Billy Jack, Merrilou—and by extension, Jimmy—was a true learning experience.

For the newlyweds, the condo they purchased in Amarillo worked fine. They found a nice three-bedroom affair in the best multi-unit development in town, possibly in all of West Texas. There wasn't much competition.

Big Hal squawked a bit at first when he forked over a substantial down payment. Then, when he saw his daughter empty her closets in their Houston spread and carted away in a moving van by a small army of laborers, he got a clearer picture of why they needed space.

"My little gal's got more clothes than Neiman Marcus," he told pals at the club, brushing off the expense. "Oh, well. You only go 'round once, right boys?"

This always got laughs, but that was before Merrilou also sent him the bill for a complete set of new furniture. Hey, a gal's got to keep up appearances.

The Burns' new home was adjacent to Amarillo's Longhorn Country Club, the only true, private golf facility in town. It had all the amenities they could want, and they quickly sailed through requirements to become members.

Merrilou considered it a step down from what she left in Houston. She was smart enough to keep opinions on that matter to herself. After all, this was Amarillo, home of the 72-ounce steak.

Happily, her new club had a tennis pro and certified yoga instructor. Also, she quickly signed up to do volunteer work for the local theatre guild.

Her new world brightened even more when, thumbing through a sorority newsletter, she discovered three alums from her old university chapter lived in Amarillo.

Though two years older, one of the alums, Crystal Kaye, overlapped with Merrilou one year in the sorority house. They quickly became lunch buddies, sharing tips, techniques, and gossip like marooned sailors on a deserted island.

Billy Jack made a special effort to be available as much as he could in Amarillo. He knew Merrilou would be spending a lot of time by herself once his basketball season got rolling. Or so he thought.

Three-day weekends became the norm in the first pre-season weeks, though he spent so much time on his cell phone—she complained— that they really were two-day weekends.

It was not unusual that, in the beginning, he made the 250-mile round trip commutes to Beaver Junction and back to Amarillo on an exhausting, daily basis.

"My conjugal visits," he joked to Jimmy. "Merrilou barely lets me through the door before we're at it."

Twice he got nailed for speeding, once in Texas and once in Oklahoma.

Each time the highway patrol officers, feeling sorry for him after Billy Jack explained the reason behind his haste, marked him down for going 10 MPH over the limit instead of the 20-plus MPH he was traveling.

Since the hefty fines came out of his own pocket, he was grateful for the discount. Each time his offer to the officers of free season tickets to Mesquite College basketball drew puzzled looks.

"Let me know if you get some tickets to rodeo, though," said the Oklahoma patrolman.

The Amarillo setup made Beaver Junction accommodations seem like something out of Little House on the Prairie. Or, to be more precise, This Old House on the Prairie.

Mesquite College was the largest property-owner in Beaver Junction. Among its holdings were a handful of off-campus buildings, which included five houses scattered about town and a multi-level commercial building on the courthouse square.

The "newest" structure in this collection was built in 1949. The school got them cheap. Most were purchased via foreclosures, and, with a minimum of expense, they were re-purposed into apartments, offices, or classrooms. None were pictured on the school's publicity brochures.

There was no problem having facilities scattered about Beaver Junction. Everything in town was within walking distance of campus.

Billy Jack and Jimmy both got assigned to what jokingly was called The Faculty Frat House. This was a huge three-story, 6,000-square foot house on the very edge of town badly in need of new roofing and a paint job.

The front yard was dead, nothing but brown grass, several forlorn trees, and tire tracks. The wrap-around wooden porch creaked with every step. There were two rocking chairs and a swing, which made it a popular gathering spot for apartment dwellers to socialize late into the night. Noisily, too.

The most distinguishing characteristic of the house's rear side was dust storms. The yard bordered a wide-open, flat prairie without a tree or hill to interrupt the horizon. There was a lengthy, cracked sidewalk leading to a hand-pump well that long ago went dry.

Originally built in the 1920s for a then-very prosperous rancher who moved to town in retirement, a local, equally-prosperous bank president bought—stole?—it for a pittance in the 1950s from the rancher's befuddled, bedridden widow.

The college got it 10 years later when the banker fled town with his secretary—male—one step ahead of Oklahoma banking regulators, who uncovered embezzlement in the low millions.

This was a huge scandal in Beaver Junction history, making even the Amarillo newspapers. Eventually the banker was discovered in Costa

Rica, extradited, and convicted in the Beaver County courthouse 200 feet from his bank.

On the day he got sentenced to jail, Mesquite College closed on his house for a pittance. He was deep into legal fees.

The Faculty Frat House was sub-divided into smaller apartments, which created awkward layouts.

Some bedrooms were huge, having been converted from living rooms. One kitchen on the top floor previously was a bathroom. One bathroom had a fireplace, which got tricky if sparks flew. Closets became showers.

Some fireplaces had wire mesh coverings. This was to prevent animals, who crawled down chimneys, from advancing inside. Each apartment was abundantly stocked with pest and rodent repellents.

The hardwood floors of the biggest apartment rooms sagged quite noticeably to the middle.

No one dared venture into the building's basement, reachable only from outside the building. Occasionally, indistinguishable noises could be heard through floorboards on the first level.

"I'm dead," Jimmy said, on the day the basketball coaches got keys and checked out their separate apartments.

"Whaddya mean?" said Billy Jack.

"No way I'm going to get some lady friend here for a visit, bro."

"Well, not to shoot you down, you're not going to be finding lady friends in this town. That's the good news."

Almost no tenant stayed more than a year in Faculty Frat House. Everyone became an early riser in the winter. At 5 a.m. daily—without fail—the hot water radiators throughout the building turned on and the pipes clanged loudly until they threw out heat.

Remember Boo Radley in *To Kill A Mockingbird*? His house? It would've been an upgrade on this.

Merrilou stayed exactly once, and that was it. The night was windy and, in addition to every other non-creature comfort, the outside shutters never stopped banging against the house.

In the future, it was decided her overnight stays would be limited to the Beaver Motel. At least the rooms got cleaned daily.

27

Getting closer

AT 2:05 P.M., I began to panic. The Sunday telephone call was scheduled for 2 p.m.

Was I supposed to call President Casey instead of him calling me? Where'd I put that number? Then at 2:07 p.m. my phone rang. Naturally, I let it ring a few more times. Can't appear too anxious.

"Phillip, sorry I'm a few minutes late at my end. Got hung up with an alum. Weekends stay pretty busy for me."

Phillip? Generally, this was where I'd interrupt and say, call me Flip.

Actually, I gave that plenty of thought when I plotted strategies for this conversation. I'd go with Phillip. Sounded more dignified, which I figured enhanced my prospects.

We traded pleasantries for the next few minutes. Turned out he wanted me to simply call him Jonathan, not President Casey. And forget the title "Doctor." He wasn't one.

He was quick to say he did not have a PhD. He had a law degree to go with an MBA, both earned at the University of Wisconsin. He got his undergrad degree in psychology at Vanderbilt. Impressive.

From the start of the call, Jonathan was someone who put you at ease in a conversation. I'm sure that's part of a college president's job description.

You had to be careful, though. Before long in these situations, you find yourself doing all the talking. That could be self-destructive in a job-seeking mode.

Better to say too little, not too much. My bartending and newspaper experience—asking questions—was a help. I asked as many questions as I answered. I had a checklist.

"So Phillip, let me cut to the chase here," he said, drawing the chit-chat to a close. "We have an opening on our faculty—the English department—and, from what I can see on your application, I think you could be a nice fit.

"If you're interested, that is, and you have not already lined something up for the Fall. I realize we're very late with this. It's not exactly what we advertised the first time, but close enough."

Interested? That would be an understatement.

My dilemma now: Did he even know I'd been rejected several months ago by his own faculty dean, Dr. D. Nelson Brunk?

"I know you've applied with us in the past," he said, answering my question (to my relief) as if he had mental telepathy. "Circumstances have changed a bit at William Harrison College. We have a new situation that has opened.

"If you still are in the market for a faculty position with us, is there a chance we could get you to Harrison for an interview.....soon? Obviously, we'll pay expenses."

Let's see. I'm still negotiating with Yale, though nothing's finalized, and, of course, I left Stanford dangling. I've yet to return that call to Princeton, and Tulane, though not top tier like the others, did offer six-figure money.

Hmmm. Yes, I think I could squeeze William Harrison College into the line of colleges seeking my services. Sheesh. I'd jump in my car now and could be there in time for dinner, if he wanted. Where is it?

Instead, we set up for the following Tuesday. Southern Indiana was not all that far from Iowa City. All I had to do was drive across Illinois.

My challenge would be to not break the speed limit.

28

The offer

As we wound up a meeting that went nearly two hours, President Casey put the ball squarely in my court. He made an offer I could refuse, but only if I was insane or had other opportunities.

On the first count, I am pretty sure I was sane. There was no doubt about the second. I didn't.

We were in his office overlooking the Harrison College campus in a building called Old Main. What college doesn't have a building called Old Main? It was beautiful, a three-story, red brick structure and one of several school buildings with landmark status.

The campus was pretty and, from my travels, would've fit quite nicely into a New England location.

There were—give or take—30 buildings. This included classrooms, labs, dormitories, athletic facilities, performance theatre, maintenance garages, guest residences, and a half-dozen or so off-campus houses that were re-purposed.

A nice, new library was in the middle of everything. This was good. I lived in libraries as a student. I loved the old Shelby Foote quote, "A university is just a group of buildings gathered around a library."

Next to it was a central dining hall in a student union, which also provided space for most student activities that had nothing to do with sports.

One building originally was a Carnegie Library. Because of its landmark status, the façade was kept intact and the interior remodeled into a museum. There also was space committed to community outreach programs.

There was no direct way to get to Harrison from Iowa City, a trek of about 450 miles. The college was in deep, deep Indiana, not far from the Ohio River. You lose an hour on the clock, too.

Flights were out of the question unless I parachuted. If I wanted to use interstate highways almost exclusively (my preference), either I drove straight South and turned left or straight East and turned right.

No matter the route, it was a full day of driving. Delightful? No.

This was late summer, however. The scenery was nice and green, and, for some reason, the Summer storms that typically strike the Ohio River Valley when I've been there did not occur.

As a bonus, winter generally comes a few weeks later here than the Upper Midwest Regions more familiar to me. They tend to be milder, too.

Since I spent Monday getting here, and arrived at dusk, there was little chance to check out the town—as if that made a difference in my decision-making process.

Ever notice: Some of the best colleges and universities are located in communities that, if the schools were not present, you wouldn't give them a second glance?

"So," said President Casey, as he brought our little confab to a conclusion, "that's my story and I'm sticking to it." He grinned.

The guy was a charmer. He smiled a lot, cracked jokes, seemed interested in everything I said, and, perhaps most important, gave great eye contact.

He actually relayed the impression that it was me, not him, in a position of strength. This made me suspicious.

The offer: Because of a late resignation in another discipline, classical languages, this gave him the money to realize his goal to add a person to what he considered an under-staffed English Dept.

He did not wish to replace the classical language position. His aim, he said, was to inject more "professionalism" and "less traditional structure" into the writing courses.

"Learning Latin is fine if you want to be a priest," he said. "That's not a priority here."

Find ways to mesh other disciplines into the curriculum. Adopt a more practical approach to English courses and writing.

Creative writing was nice, he observed. It generally did not lead to jobs, however. Students needed to be exposed to additional aspects of the writing industry. He wanted to attach writing to every discipline.

At a salary of $70,000, I would receive a one-year contract. Officially, I would be considered a visiting, or interim, instructor. If everything went well, the slot would turn into a more secure, tenure track position next year.

Though I did not have a doctorate, a usual pre-requisite, I could apply and get the "strongest" consideration with my MFA, which, after all, was a terminal degree.

President Casey did not quite wink when he used the description "strongest consideration," but he made it clear. I was a front-runner in a one-person race.

In other words, do not rock the boat. Don't screw up. Remember. Colleges hate to go through lengthy, expensive searches, something I was learning first-hand.

Me in a strong position? Little did the president know, or so I thought.

Yes, Rick offered me a modest raise not to leave the Airport when I told him about the Indiana opportunity. But think about it: Remain a bartender vs. full-time slot teaching in a college. Duhhh.

One formality remained. He wanted me to interview the next day with the faculty dean, D. Nelson Brunk, who turned me down on the first Harrison application.

Should be interesting. It was.

29

2d interview

"I'D LIKE TO make it clear at the start," said Dean Brunk. "It is nothing personal, but hiring you was not my idea. I filled that first English position you applied for with someone I thought better qualified. She had a PhD. It's as simple as that.

"In this case, I am not in favor of adding another position to my English department. It's coming at the expense of not filling the slot caused by a resignation in the Classics Department, though I suppose we save money on salaries.

"This means there will be no one on my faculty to teach Latin, something I consider imperative in a liberal arts education. Like I said: This is nothing personal, mind you."

A dozen or so wisecracks went through my mind. They don't call me Flip for nothing.

I remained quiet, mustering what I would call an oh-so slight, neutral-looking smile. Today, I would play the Phillip card and not be Flip.

"President Casey seems to be quite certain this is the direction he wants to take us, and it's too late to mount a regular search," the good Dean continued.

"He's correct on the second count. By the way, Jonathan is the third, no fourth, president in the time I've been here."

Nice to know you're wanted. Well, maybe that's a bit harsh. He was being honest, I guess, and I gave him that.

He certainly had a nice office. It was huge, larger than Casey's and with a gorgeous, polished wood finish. There was a private bathroom.

His desk was big enough for ping-pong. There were pictures everywhere of the good dean posing with VIPs, from governors of Indiana to U.S. cabinet members. Oddly, there was one of him shaking hands with actress Betty White.

Hanging on the wall behind his desk was a portrait of the dean and his wife, Mildred, and a framed copy of his PhD degree (in classics) from the University of Connecticut.

Only a fireplace was missing.

The interview, if it could be called that, was short. He talked, I listened.

Mostly he told me about himself and what he considered intrinsic values to an undergraduate education. At the top of his list: A heavy dose of classics, philosophy, and art history.

"The liberal arts are more important than ever before," he said. "We're in the business of teaching young Americans how to think.

"We're not an employment service. Subjects like Latin and Greek remain a priority. With me, anyhow."

Was I in the middle of some sort of academic turf war?

When our meeting was over, the dean walked me to the adjoining office of his personal administrator. He left instructions, turned, and walked back to his office. No handshake, and no "welcome aboard."

The harried looking, 30ish administrator, Anne, watched her boss go into his office. When he disappeared behind the door, she turned, looked at me, flashed a quick, conspiratorial smile, and said: "Not a good day."

She got nothing from me. I was happy to be hired.

I spent the next hour filling out forms, packed Anne's handouts into my newly-purchased briefcase (every college teacher has to have a briefcase), and took notes on her instructions.

As I completed my paperwork, Anne handed a note to me: President Casey wanted a brief chat at the end of the day.

30

The back story

MY FINAL ROUND-UP with President Casey lasted maybe 15 minutes, but was very illuminating. In effect, this was a pep talk.

It became more obvious that lines were being drawn at good, old William H. Harrison College. He didn't get specific. He didn't name names. He didn't make promises.

Everything was nuanced, but it was obvious I was stepping into something here that did not meet the eye.

The president, in only his second year as head man, wanted change. He wanted the school to shake loose old ways of doing things. He wanted to *modernize* (his word) the liberal arts approach, tailor it to better meet students' changing occupational needs in the 21st Century.

More internships. More experiential learning. All on a tight budget, of course.

Apparently, I was getting a second meeting for a reason: He wanted me to go see the campus for myself, meet other staff. He was confident that, after that, I would serve on his front lines.

"I looked closely at your resume," he said. "You have nice, practical experience to bring to students. I saw your article in USA Today and read other things you've done. You've been a busy, productive person in a short time period.

"It's great, to me, to see balance between real world and teaching. This is what we need in our classes. In fact, I've looked closely at a lot of the resumes of applicants for jobs here over the last year, whether we hired them or not.

"Heck, you could coach basketball from what I saw, given your inter-scholastic playing days at Lake Forest, China and Iowa City."

We both laughed. Mine was more forced.

"In fact," he continued, "your time spent teaching in China fairly jumps out at me. I am very interested in planting some international footprints. We've done very little in this regard."

Then, quickly turning serious, he added: "I think we missed too many opportunities in the past to add energy here at Harrison. I don't wish to do that in the future."

He was not laughing.

31

Bon voyage

RICK TOOK THE news OK that I was departing the Airport, like tomorrow.

Part of our original bartending agreement was 24-hour notice for me to leave. ("Resign" sounds a little over-the-top for a bartender.) He could get temporary help. There would be no shortage of students wanting to rent an apartment above a lively bar.

His biggest concern was this: He was losing me as the player/coach of the Airport basketball team.

"Damn," was his immediate, unvarnished response to my news. "You really had it going after you took over last season. I figured we'd have great momentum this season."

Since I already had signed a lease for a place in Harrison, I was anxious to get packed and hit the road. The school year there was only a few weeks away.

My Airport farewell party was harried and short, but fun. It was on a Saturday afternoon in one, large corner of the bar. Half the people there were simply customers, who had no idea they were participating in an event. They saw free cake and went for it.

David James, my counselor in the Iowa Writer's Workshop, attended. He was a nice touchstone through my journeys.

He seemed genuinely pleased I'd landed a real college teaching job, possibly tired of writing so many letters of recommendation

Generously, David acted as if I were headed for the Ivy League instead of Harrison College in Indiana.

"Hamilton College, a perfect entry spot with a strong reputation," he declared. "You couldn't ask for anything better….better than my first gig, Bismarck Junior College."

Hamilton? No, David, Harrison. I let it slide. At least they started with the same letter.

Jeff Richards, my favorite defense attorney and spinner of great tales on slow Airport weekday afternoons, was there long enough to eat some cake, drink a beer, and handed me his card. Several of them, actually.

"Give me a call if you need some legal advice," he said. "I'm licensed to practice in Indiana, too. I'll give you a discount."

IV

32

Howdy, Buckaroos

IN MEN'S COLLEGE basketball, it is not unusual that successful teams get overshadowed by the school's football program.

Cases in point: Notre Dame, Texas, Southern Cal, Texas A&M, and every school in the Southeastern Conference except Kentucky and Vanderbilt.

In his basketball travels, Billy Jack was well aware of this. What he never envisioned at Mesquite, or any school, was this: Townspeople and alums got most excited over the college's rodeo program.

Rodeo?

"It's a sport?" said Jimmy, when he first learned this and wondered out loud to Billy Jack. "I never knew that. You mean riding horses and cows and roping and all that cowboy shit? They do that here?"

Yes, they did—and quite well.

Billy Jack knew there was a rodeo program at Mesquite. His first hint was the school's nickname for its sports teams: Buckaroos.

Then, his soon-to-be athletic director, Branch Wilson, made a point of telling him early in the interview process there was a Mesquite rodeo program. He left out the part about it being a big deal.

In fact, Mesquite was a member of the National Collegiate Rodeo Association (NCRA). It was not an NCAA sport, which meant there were unlimited scholarships and few rules to govern recruiting, eligibility and competition.

And Mesquite handed out scholarships like candy. Why not? Tuition was cheap. They were a good investment. The sport attracted sponsors.

The remaining Mesquite sports teams, like basketball and baseball, competed in Division III of the NCAA, which forbids athletic scholarships to be awarded unlike Division I and II.

This made things tough for ambitious, D3 coaches. At Mesquite, Billy Jack discovered things could be even tougher. The campus heroes would be Buckaroos who roped steers and rode a horse, not scored baskets and grabbed rebounds.

Furthermore, the sport siphoned off a large chunk of the athletic budget. There were rodeo teams for both men *and* women.

"Girls do this stuff, too?" asked Jimmy, whose only experience with horses was, as a kid growing up in Chicago, seeing mounted policemen in St. Patrick's Day parades.

"What do they call them? The Buckarettes?"

The school maintained its own 150-acre ranch several miles from town. Few expenses were spared. The site occasionally hosted rodeos on the pro circuit and NCRA regional competitions.

Once, back in the 1970s, the U.S. national championships were held here.

In addition to barns, there were corrals, miles and miles of fence to maintain, farmhouse, stables, tack rooms filled with saddles, locker rooms, trophy room for boosters, and a stadium with a scoreboard.

There was lots of livestock, over 100 head of horses, ponies, and cattle. This included prized bulls and stallions used for breeding, which provided a tidy revenue stream for the college.

(The irony was not lost on Billy Jack: Many universities had major headaches with athletes arrested for sexual abuse, but Mesquite actually made money with a stud service. What a concept!)

The Buckaroo rodeo staff consisted of two full-time coaches, two part-time assistant coaches, trainer, full-time horse-shoer, and two maintenance men, one of whom mostly collected and carted off manure to be recycled into fertilizer sold in five-pound bags at the concession stand during events. There also was a part-time veterinarian.

Overseeing the program was Hank Harkin, a tough, old bird born on a Texas ranch and who rode horses almost as soon as he could walk. Officially, he was an associate athletic director.

Numerous Mesquite alums went on to professional rodeo circuits.

One, Toby Ballard, appeared in a dozen Hollywood westerns mostly in supporting roles as a bad guy. He was a revered member of the school's athletic hall of fame.

Perhaps the school's most famous rodeo alum, Crash Henderson, is in the film industry's Stuntmen's Hall of Fame. His specialty was falling off galloping horses at full speed, usually as a marauding Indian.

Sadly, while plying this specialty in a spaghetti western shot in Italy in the 1960s, his horse pulled up suddenly, Crash went flying over the animal's head, and broke his neck. He died instantly.

Friends and family were outraged when the film's director left the footage of Crash's fall in the final cut. In a moving memorial service at Mesquite, Henderson's ashes were sprinkled in the main Buckaroo corral.

"Maybe rodeo isn't such a bad thing," said Billy Jack, who almost always chose to stay positive when facing obstacles. "I got some ideas how we can move some pieces, maybe even make it work for us.

"Trust me."

33

Tricks

"I DON'T GET it. Now I'm an admissions counselor? What's the deal? I'm a basketball coach, aren't I?"

Jimmy was awed when Billy Jack explained what he had in mind.

"It's simple, Jimmy," he said. "Obviously, you're here to be my assistant coach and you will coach. I need you. Nothing's changed. But on paper, you're listed as an admissions counselor. I worked it out with the school.

"Why? See, admission counselors can recruit students anytime. Basketball coaches can't. The NCAA rules put a lot of limitations on us. But someone from admissions is free to have as many personal contacts as it takes to get a student."

Billy Jack had stockpiled ideas like this—a coach masquerading as an admissions counselor—his entire, albeit young, career.

Now, at Mesquite, his first head coaching job, he planned to put many in play. He showed the applicable NCAA rule to Jimmy.

Contact by Coach Employed in Admissions Office. It is permissible for a coach who is employed in the admissions office of the institution to be involved in off-campus admissions programs directed at prospective students in general, provided contact made with a prospective student-athlete before the completion of his or her sophomore year in high school is not for the purpose of athletics recruitment (e.g., athletics recruiting presentation).

"Who's to say what your conversations are about," he said. "Nobody'll be taping them. Hell, you can gather up a bunch of high school kids and give 'em a Mesquite pitch. And, oh, by the way, they just happen to play basketball."

Billy Jack became quite familiar with NCAA regulations in the weeks leading up to the school year. The rule book was his favorite nighttime reading.

"Too bad it isn't books on tape," said Merrilou. "You could listen to it when you drive back and forth to Amarillo."

Getting basketball players good enough to win an NCAA title was the challenge.

Why would they come to Mesquite? To become a Buckaroo? There were no scholarships, little exposure, no glamour, no car as a bonus, and nothing in it for parents or siblings.

Oh, incidentally, the college is in the middle of nowhere, in a town called Beaver Junction, the Cow Chip Throwing Capital of the World.

The nearest town of consequence (and surely you're familiar with the bright lights of Amarillo) is a mere two hours away—across boring, flat, and mostly uninhabited prairie.

That's the bad news. The good news?

Well the NCAA rules may be tight in areas, like scholarships, but they were extremely loose elsewhere in Division III ranks.

For instance, transfer students don't have to sit out a year like they do in upper divisions. They become instantly eligible. This definitely could come in handy.

He'd gladly welcome a player who'd been bounced, for whatever reason, from a major school program. Step right up lad. We've got a spot for you on our roster. No fuss, no muss. You can play now.

There was virtually no scrutiny by the NCAA at this lowly level, too. If the Buckaroos break rules, a lock now that Billy Jack was on the scene, the whistle would need to be blown—with proof—by another school.

The NCAA itself did not police small colleges. Just keep the paperwork in order, guys, and don't blow the deadlines. That's all it wanted.

Academics? Eligibility? Surely you jest? Billy Jack had answers for that, too.

"The deal is this, Jimmy," he explained. "The school sets the standards to be eligible to compete. Athletes have to take at least 12 credit hours during a term, but the GPA (grade point average) to play is what we say it is.

"You think those rodeo dudes are Phi Beta Kappa's?"

This rule was boldly underlined in his NCAA manual.

Good Academic Standing. To be eligible to represent an institution in intercollegiate athletics competition, a student-athlete shall be in good academic standing as determined by the academic authorities who determine the meaning of such phrases for all students of the institution, subject to controlling legislation of the conference(s) or similar association of which the institution is a member.

Jimmy was impressed. The coach had everything covered—and then some.

"Want to know my favorite move?" said Billy Jack.

"I'm not just coaching at Mesquite. I'm teaching. The school's giving me faculty status because of my advanced degree, the masters I got as a grad assistant. This means I can teach courses, also set up some independent study."

"You really want to do that, too?" asked Jimmy.

Of course, explained Billy Jack. It's a way to give players A's to help their grade point averages. They could also take at least one independent study course from him, adding another A to their portfolio.

"You want to try to keep the team's overall GPA as high as you can. It's good public relations. I intend to save a couple spots on the roster for kids with really good grades, though they're not going to play."

"Damn, bro," said Jimmy. "You really have thought of everything. What would you teach?"

"Oh, hell, I don't know. I'll think of something. I got a few weeks to put it together."

Academia 101

THE FIRST NIGHT in my new Harrison apartment I slept in a sleeping bag on the floor. The second night I slept in a new bed I purchased that day along with other residential necessities, such as silverware, toilet paper, and coffee.

My first William H. Harrison College faculty meeting went well, too. I guess.

There were about 50 of us assembled in the Jordan Science Center's lecture hall. Men outnumbered women by a sizable margin. Older men outnumbered younger men by a wider margin.

I sat in the rear, listened, and stood when I was introduced as one of the newbies. My name was misspelled on my nametag—Philip instead of Phillip—but no complaints. I've been called worse.

President Casey made a brief welcoming remark, and then disappeared. From start to finish, this was Dean Brunk's show.

There were announcements, clarifications and a short film about the college produced by the theatre department. No one took notes. I thought I heard someone softly snoring soon after lights went out for the video.

Faculty members also learned committee assignments for the year. I got Admissions & Enrollment. This meant that I would be in a group that included Harrison's director of admissions, a trustee, staff member, one alum, and a student.

Our particular mission: Keep things moving smoothly and explore ways to maintain—if not increase—our numbers without lowering standards any more than necessary.

I assumed this was a committee low on the totem pole in the eyes of my veteran colleagues, certainly not as prestigious as the others. Also, unlike most faculty committees, it meant work with quantifiable results.

The others were: Scholarship, Technology, Athletics, Buildings & Grounds, Campus Culture, Curriculum, Diversity, Tenure, and Alumni.

From what little I gathered on this day, Campus Culture was the most envied. Every year, it took an expense-paid, one-week trip to another college to "study its integration of the arts into daily living."

Invariably the schools visited, all in the dead of the Indiana winter, were in Florida or Southern California. It was not unusual for committee members to bring golf clubs, tennis rackets, and beach garb.

On the flip side, I was told assignment to the Alumni Committee could be a pain in the butt. This meant placating do-gooder alums, typically successful businessmen and lawyers, and their notions of learning and what should be taught in classrooms. Occasionally, this called for faculty to deviate from syllabi that served them well for years or, in some cases, decades.

Dean Brunk introduced some topics—apparently ongoing from last year—to be explored as the new academic year progressed.

High on the list seemed to be faculty pay raises. Others were: Shortening the school year, fewer classroom contact hours, and shortening the period tenured professors had to wait to go on sabbatical.

One youngish professor introduced the idea of adding a holiday to the academic calendar—an observance of the gay rights movement. This should be, he said on Oct. 11, which was established already as National Coming Out Day.

The room seemed equally divided: One-third nodded approvingly, one-third smirked, and the other third appeared ambivalent, or too busy looking at their iPhones to know what was being discussed.

One professor said it would never fly, considering Oct. 12 was Columbus

Day. "Two successive days off, one celebrating gay rights and 24 hours later one for the alleged discovery of America?" he noted. "Good luck with that." This drew laughter.

In fact, I would come to learn the Harrison College calendar was loaded with holidays. The school celebrated two in February—President's Day and its own, special Tippecanoe Day, which always was Feb. 9, the birthday (in 1773) of the school's namesake, President William H. Harrison.

The biggest buzz during the meeting occurred when the Dean announced the names of two Harrison professors granted academic tenure. This woke up everyone, drawing a lively round of applause and, later, handshakes all around.

My Harrison office was in Durham Hall, which was home to the English Dept. offices and classrooms as well as several smaller departments. My space was in the basement, along with a half-dozen others.

This was an OK location except for a couple of things. I was next to the boiler room, which made terrific noise every time it started up when the weather turned cold.

Also, I was adjacent to the men's room and that meant plenty of toilet flushes. Additionally, I could hear the hand dryer, which meant I knew who washed and who didn't. Hey. This was valuable information when it came to handshakes.

There was, however, a ground level window that gave me an excellent view of ankles and feet of everyone using the sidewalk leading to Durham. Occasionally, squirrels foraging for nuts in the window well peeked into my office.

Prof. Shackelford, who'd been the department chairman since about the time the Declaration of Independence got signed, was on Durham Hall's main floor. Rumor had it he remained on the job as a favor to Dean Brunk, who hated uncertainty.

He met with me holding a half-blank check. He wanted me to teach a general Intro to English class—read standards published no later than the 19th century. We're talking Dickens, Shakespeare, Chaucer, and the boys, etc.

Zzzzz. Frankly, this bored me to tears. I agreed to do it without objection.

On the other hand, he had no idea about a second course for me to teach. My appearance on the faculty was unexpected, since I replaced someone in a different department.

Did I have ideas?

My proposal to teach a pure, general writing course for underclassmen—something that bordered on simple composition—got met with lines across his forehead.

"Our incoming students can write," he responded, rather indignantly. "We look at their entrance essays quite closely."

I wanted to say: Who wrote them?

I was well aware there are plenty of services out there in the business of providing assistance in writing entrance essays. I had done it myself as a favor to parents eager to get kids into good schools.

It also had been my brief experience that, as a teaching assistant who graded hundreds of undergrad papers, younger students fell apart when called on to write something on their own that was longer than a Tweet.

But I did not say these things. I continued to play the role of Phillip, not Flip.

There was a way around this with the chairman, of course.

"I am sure all Harrison students are good writers," I told him. "If that's what I find in a freshman class, I'll just keep raising the bar as we proceed through the term. We'll get into both long and short form formats in depth. Maybe even dabble at poetry."

Rather reluctantly, after a 10-minute exchange, he agreed with a deep sigh to let me "run wild," as he put it, with my second class. Nevertheless, he was quick to point out this was unprecedented in his Harrison tenure.

Shackelford was in the front row, with other department chairs, at that opening faculty meeting. He smiled and we chatted a bit afterward. He seemed tired. I was happy he recognized me. The nametag probably helped.

While the meeting seemed perfunctory, the reception was quite lively. Free food and drinks, including wine, helped.

Mostly I cruised the room, smiling, gravitating a bit toward other rookies, and eavesdropped on conversations among the veterans. I spotted four jackets, two tweed and two corduroy, with elbow patches.

Everyone but us rookies seemed to know each other. What did you do in the summer seemed to be a common thread.

A few favorites: Grant-supported study in Paris; short teaching gig, including housing, at another college in Manhattan; lecturing on a Greek Island cruise ship; golf; grant-supported book research in the British Museum; playing the clarinet at the Santa Fe Opera; and docent for walking tours in Rome.

Teaching in college was looking better and better. It beat spending summers serving pitchers of beer in a tavern to sweaty softball players.

35

Lights, camera, action

THE DEVELOPMENT OF the Internet is the world's greatest invention, greater than the wheel, gunpowder, combustible engines, and Arizona Iced Tea.

No one knows this more than college coaches with tight budgets. Social media devices such as YouTube, email, Twitter, Instagram, and Skype, to name a few, were great for their recruiting of athletes. Cheap, too.

Oh, the big boys at Duke, Kentucky, UCLA, and Kansas never sweated scouting and harvesting prospects. With unlimited resources, including boosters' deep pockets, they gather enough film and background checks to produce documentaries on their recruits. Lots of visits.

For the small schools, it always was a crapshoot. They had neither staff nor funds to chase prospects. Often, there wasn't a personal, up-close view of a recruit until he or she showed up at the school year's start.

Imagine the surprise when Joe Blow, touted by his high school coach as the next Michael Jordan, turned out to be 5-feet-6 instead of 6-feet-5 when he walked through the he door?

Now, thanks to new technology, instead of looking at grainy, three-week old film of Bell & Howell quality generally shot by a 15-year-old team manager, they could see games live on their phones. They talked directly to prospects and saw them face-to-face at the same time. They got all the video needed.

Yes, indeed, new media was the great equalizer.

Billy Jack had a plan to take it to another level. This would be a contribution to college sports that might be discussed for generations to come—his *pièce de résistance*, if you will.

If all else failed, it might signal a future for him in Hollywood.

Billy Jack explained that he and Jimmy would do a fair share of traveling to recruit. Most of this would be concentrated in major, regional cities, such as Dallas, San Antonio, Oklahoma City, Phoenix and Denver. This would allow "lots of one-stop shopping," see many games on one trip.

But he also wanted to do a large share of video teleconferencing, a spinoff of Skype, to stay in touch with recruits. He wanted to focus this approach on promising players in remote, singular, and harder-to-visit regions—Walla Walla, Duluth, Bangor, Rapid City, etc.

These would be the kids that did not get much personal contact with coaches. Furthermore, it would be expensive for them to visit the campus. "Don't other coaches give them teleconference calls, too?" asked Jimmy.

"Sure, but we're going to add some flair," said Billy Jack. "We're going to add backdrops the kid can see over my shoulder while we're talking.

"They're going to be like theatre scenery. I got the idea the other night when Merrilou dragged me to a musical in Amarillo."

Billy Jack went on to explain backdrops he had in mind while talking to recruits:

1. A luxurious looking locker room (which Mesquite didn't have) with the prospect's name over a locker fronted by a padded rocking chair;

2. A window looking out on a horizon filled with babbling brooks, beautiful, snow-capped mountains and grazing horses;

3. A huge trophy case filled with awards, autographed pictures, framed certificates, and trophies.

"We can find graphics easy enough on the Internet, and then we'll Photoshop the images we want for background sizes," said Billy Jack. "They won't be that hard to put together."

It's for sure, he concluded, everything would show better than what the college really had to offer: A crammed locker room, toilet stalls with no doors, and cold showers; an isolated setting on a barren prairie; and no basketball trophies of note, only those for rodeo.

"I like it, a lot," said Jimmy. "You know what else you can do? Make sure you mix them up, too. Make multiple calls to a kid, but rotate backgrounds."

Said Billy Jack: "Good thinking. I like it. We're on a roll."

36

Casey, at bat

THERE WERE SIX of us invited to President Casey's office on the Saturday morning after that first faculty meeting. Four women, two men. Nice odds.

All of us were new to William H. Harrison College's teaching ranks. The meeting was very relaxed. Apparently, the president wanted to make sure the newbies met each other.

I had no trouble relating to Charley Cunningham, the other male in our group. He was the new men's basketball coach, married, two pre-schoolers, and a Harrison alum.

Charley, from the same Louisville neighborhood as Muhammad Ali, was a basketball star for the Colonials. He spent several years playing professionally in Australia, returned to the U.S., worked his way up assistant coaching ranks, and answered his alma mater's call for this first head job.

"I love the place, but it does seem a bit weird to be back here," he confided later to me. "The faculty's practically all the same professors from my student days, and I wasn't the best student. Even the old equipment manager, Peck, is still here. And crabby as ever."

You had to feel for him. He definitely felt pressure. He was the first African-American to star big time—Little All-American—for a

Harrison sports team. Now, he was the first African-American to become a head coach here.

The women in the room? Two were single, I'd find out. One was a newlywed and the other I ranked as "sexuality-to-be-determined."

Mary Jagger—no relation to Mick, I asked, she frowned, rolled her eyes—was in sociology, possessor of a new PhD from Arizona State University in Tempe.

I learned Mary, single, was a real "boots on the ground" practitioner, whose specialty was immigration. Her dissertation focused on Mexican border issues.

I spent a fair amount of time in our meeting wondering where her excellent tan lines ended. When I got caught staring, she smiled, but no adjustment. Progress.

Michelle Wickett was here to teach business courses, or, as she put it, microeconomics. She was on the tenure track, so I presumed she had a doctorate. No glass ceilings for her. Get out of her way.

Sherry York, married, was in education. Harrison cranked out its share of secondary and elementary teachers. She was to coordinate— ramp up?—student teaching assignments. No kids, and a hubby finishing a PhD 100 miles away at Indiana U. He spent many hours in his car.

Patricia ("not Pat, please") Mills was the new head librarian. Harrison had a beautiful facility in the Grabbe Library, but in real need of some upgrades.

Patricia was here to oversee that and, in a first for the school, teach a course in library science. It was to be called—are you sitting down?— "Introduction to Organizing & Retrieving Information 101." She had been a head librarian for several years at a community college before this job.

One of her "assignments" also was to build some bridges to the local community with outreach programs. The town still used a library over a hundred years old, and it would not be a great leap to think its current librarians were there when it opened.

President Casey had a tray full of goodies for us, and presented each with a different book that he somehow—and successfully—surmised would appeal to us based on our individual backgrounds.

Mine was "Zen In The Art of Writing" by Ray Bradbury, who, to me, was one of the great writers in modern literature. I mean, not only could this guy write, he invented a whole, new genre, science fiction. While I'd read some of his work, I'd never read this book. It was on my "get" list.

Bradbury could write in every form. Furthermore, he was totally self-taught and never attended college. He explained it this way once to the Paris Review: "You can't learn to write in college. It's a very bad place for writers because the teachers always think they know more than you do – and they don't."

Not exactly a ringing endorsement for academia, a world I now was jumping into with both feet. I decided then and there I would not loan it to students.

It was uncanny that President Casey would know to get that for me, the perfect selection. It showed exactly the right touch of irreverence and rebellion, quirks I began to feel we shared.

Did the others in the room get the same vibe? If so, Harrison College was getting more and more interesting with each meeting.

This was my second confab with him and I'd barely set foot in a classroom. I'm sure this was the same for the other five.

I was becoming familiar with his office. Compared to Dean Brunk's, it was quite unkempt. Papers were piled on his desk as well as on two tables.

There were PCs within reach on both sides of his desk, in addition to photos of his family, one of his Harrison inauguration and framed certificates of his MBA and law degrees from Wisconsin.

Curiously, a glass encased baseball bat was on the wall over his head. Casey, at the bat?

The president was starting only his second year at good old Harrison. He had been provost at Towson State in Maryland, a large, public school that had a reputation for staying relevant in liberal arts with innovative programs.

Rumor had it that his hiring here involved a big tussle among trustees, two of whom resigned after the dust settled. His support came from the board's new wave, including the chair.

The other finalist for the job? None other than Dean D. Nelson Brunk, who'd been interim president for the year before the appointment.

"I'm from the Midwest originally, Indianapolis actually, so this was an opportunity to get back to familiar turf," President Casey told us. "I'm very excited about what we can do here. We're near several large cities. I think we can do a better job leveraging this."

Translation: Harrison was a bit sleepy and needed a kick in the ass. While Casey did not come right out and say it, this implication was obvious.

"The small, private liberal arts colleges are facing huge challenges," said the president, a comment I'm sure he'd made at least a thousand times in his short tenure. "The gap's getting wider and wider. Technology is a big reason.

"But technology can be our friend if we're willing to embrace it. We can use it to overcome whatever lack of resources we may have. In the end, we owe it to our students. Their parents pay big bucks for them to be here. We can never forget that."

He made it pretty clear our little group was anointed as some sort of Swat Squad, fresh faces with hands-on backgrounds and experiential approaches.

We replaced professors who'd retired, not moved on. We were new blood. He hoped to find more of us as openings occurred in coming years.

At least twice he told us we were the first instructors to get his individual attention in the hiring process.

I was not sure how to interpret that. I wanted to think he had our backs if things got edgy with department chairs—like me trying to get a simple writing course off the ground.

As we broke up, President Casey said: "I feel I've been doing all the talking here. Frankly, I get kind of excited thinking what we (we?) can do here. Do you any of you have last, unrelated questions for me?"

With this, I made a transition from Phillip to Flip. I was quick to raise my hand.

What's the deal with the baseball bat? I asked.

"Oh, wow, glad someone wanted to know," he said. "It's a bat used in a game by Hank Aaron when he played in Indianapolis, my home town. He's an all-time baseball hero in our family. My dad saw him play a lot in Indy one summer and bought it at a charity auction.

Well, he was my hero, too, and I knew his statistics cold in the Major Leagues as well as the minor leagues. He never played in Indianapolis.

Should I ask about that? Flip or Phillip? Again I went with Flip, and said: "I don't want to break a bubble here, but I do not recall him playing for Indianapolis."

"Ah, but he did, Phillip, and I'm glad you questioned that. He spent three months one season playing for the Indianapolis Clowns in the last years of the Negro American League. That was where he was scouted and signed to a Major League contract by the Braves."

Whoa. Too cool. A college president who treasured a signed baseball bat used by Hank Aaron when he played in the Negro League.

This guy was growing on me.

Discovering Whitey's

TIME TO SAMPLE Harrison nightlife.

After a full day of meetings on a Friday, plus more class prep and putting finishing touches on my apartment on Saturday, I headed for downtown to see exactly what this southern Indiana community of 11,392 had to offer in the way of a social experience.

Not much.

There was an old, dusty movie house, The Strand, that offered nothing released within the past two years. I stepped inside the local bowling alley, Hoosier Land Lanes. There was a short order grill, and a bank of video games seeing more action than anything on its eight lanes.

The liveliest, remaining choices seemed to be any of three taverns on the courthouse square.

The first, Keg Town, was full of students streaming into town for the first week of classes. The place was crammed full of "how was your summer" reunions that promised to extend into the dormitories after last call.

Thanks, but no. If there is one thing I knew headed into my first, full-time college teaching position, don't go into bars heavily frequented by students. Nothing good can happen.

If coeds aren't parading their boobs to get attention, a sure ticket to disaster, any student there thinks he or she shares a secret bond with a teacher if they're drinking under the same roof.

This is truly so if you end up swapping alcohol-fueled anecdotes into the night. From my bartending in Iowa City, I knew this to be trouble.

The Airport was a favorite of "adults" and "townies," though on weekends there always was spillover from the student body. Generally, their added presence resulted in a faculty exodus.

Why? Because it's important to keep a line between you and the students, some of whom you'll be grading—and all of whom think they do "A" work.

In theatre, it's called the aesthetic difference and means the actors—or, in this case, teachers—are on one side. The students—or audience—are on the other side. The line should not be crossed.

My old Iowa workshop counselor, David James, warned me of this dynamic. I saw it play out many times in the Airport, where profs traveled in packs.

"It's for protection from students," he explained to me. "If you want to get sloshed, do it at faculty dinner parties in the privacy of a home. They'll drive you to drink."

Inexplicably, the second tavern, Russell's, had one, lonely customer sitting at the far end of the bar in a conversation with the bartender. They both looked up when I opened the door.

"Closing in 20 minutes," the bartender called out. "Try Whitey's."

The third joint, The Roadhouse, seemed even busier, but with one caveat. There were about 20 motorcycles, mostly muscle jobs with high handlebars, parked in front.

I peeked inside. Bruce Springsteen was blasting away. Two people were dancing on the pool table, each with a long ponytail and in their underwear.

Otherwise there were more leather jackets, tattoos, cutoff t-shirts and head scarves than you'd see at a Harley-Davidson convention. This would not do either.

As I backed away from the door, a voice called out from the rear of the cluster of motorcycles parked in front: "It's not for the weak at heart, Pilgrim. Better move on."

Pilgrim?

I shouted back, "John Wayne, 1962 in 'The Man Who Shot Liberty Valance.' It's probably one of his best lines. To be precise, it goes: 'Whoa. Take 'er easy there, Pilgrim.'"

There was silence.

While he apparently sized me up, I could see a quick glow of red in the darkness from a puff on a cigar. He dismounted his parked cycle, slowly made his way toward me in the darkness and emerged like a woolly mammoth from a cave.

Whoops. Did my Flip side get me in trouble this time?

The guy was huge. He had to be 6-foot-5, maybe 250 pounds, and with a flaming red moustache, beard with a tightly-wound braid down the middle and hair way past his shoulders.

He wore a sleeveless leather vest and had more artwork on his bulging arms than the Prado. His muscles had muscles. His wallet was attached to a long chain hooked to a belt loop in front.

He stood staring down at me, took another puff from his cigar, and, thankfully, turned to exhale to one side away from my face.

Then, he stuck out his hand and said, "My name's Nate Stine. You're new here, aint'cha? You with the college?"

We got my status settled in quick order. Yes, I was new. Yes, I would be teaching English at the local college. Yes, I knew some of John Wayne's best lines as well as those of other, classic film stars. I quoted a few for him.

We stood there chatting for nearly a half-hour. Several of his buddies came out to take leaks in the alley. The lines were too long inside to hold it, and each acknowledged Nate while he talked to the stranger.

Turns out Nate was part of a motorcycle gang called, and I am not joking here, the Holy Rollers. Their history, I learned, was definitely not holy and well-known to local law enforcement officials.

Most mischief occurred in the Louisville area and other parts of northern Kentucky, though Nate, their leader, was from Evansville.

The Holy Rollers' home base was in a tiny nearby Indiana town called Tennyson, where they'd gather on weekends to plot their "excursions."

Their compound was a farmhouse where Rollers could crash or use for a hideout—mostly from their "old ladies" or outstanding warrants. A barn was used as storage for motorcycles and assorted tools and spare parts. Another farm building was full of weightlifting and workout equipment.

Three times in the last two years the place was raided by the DEA. They always came up empty, but each time promised to return.

"We like to think of ourselves as a civic organization, sort of like a Rotary Club on wheels," he said. "'Course, others might not quite see it that way. I tried to get us organized as a church, but the IRS didn't agree.

"Imagine that."

His nickname was "Preacher," owing to his role as the Holy Roller's head honcho. The rank-and-file were Deacons. I got the feeling he was a bit bored by the bar scene inside The Roadhouse. He wanted to talk.

He'd played football for a year at Indiana before quitting. "Grades were OK," he added quickly. "Just seemed like a waste of time. Got tired of coaches in my face all the time. Seemed silly.

"Besides, bro, they wanted me to stop riding my chopper. Said I could get hurt. Bullshit."

Nate stuck around the IU campus, took a few courses, and then began working in construction. "Suits me fine, gives me weeks off between jobs and money's good. Lots of time to work out. Proper."

He was interested to discover this was my first college teaching position, asked numerous questions about what would take place in my courses, and wanted to know books we'd read.

Definitely, this guy was more than Rambo.

Finally, we shook hands and he hit me with this: "Do me a favor, Flipper Man or whatever. Keep an eye on my daughter. Name's Kate, she's a freshman this year. That's why I guided my crew here this weekend. Thought maybe I'd catch a glimpse of her. I don't get to see her much."

"That's rough, Nate. You and Kate's mother divorced?"

"Never married. Now she's taken up with some asshole. He doesn't care to see me, so I stay away just to keep peace. I miss my Kate, though.

Bright. Fun to talk to, maybe has a real future if she can get out of the house."

I agreed to keep an eye on Kate, if our paths crossed. Nate said her last name was McDonald, same as her mother's.

Somehow, as the offspring of the man standing in front of me, I had a notion she'd be recognizable on the campus. Maybe she played field hockey. Or threw the shot put.

As I walked away, Nate added: "And if you're looking for a place to hang out, forget these places in Harrison. Try Whitey's out in the country. I'm guessing it's more your speed."

"Thanks, Pilgrim," I answered. We both laughed.

That was the second recommendation for Whitey's in one night. Since it was several miles from town, I decided to take a pass. I was tired.

If Rule No. 1 was don't imbibe with students, Rule No. 2 was keep your drinking within walking distance of where you sleep.

The last thing I wanted at this stage was my name on a police blotter.

38

School daze

Pedagogy (noun): The method and practice of teaching, especially as an academic subject or theoretical concept.

MY TWO HARRISON classes in the first semester were both M-W-F, and one hour apiece. The writing class would meet at 9 a.m. The afternoon class—an introduction to classic English authors, principally Shakespeare—was scheduled for 1 p.m.

Here's one trouble spot with Friday classes. It's a little-known secret that the three-day weekend was invented by college students, who like to get a head start on their social life Thursday night.

This means they are not in shape for Friday classes—if they appear at all. They frequently doze off. Many routinely depart for weekend trips home, or wherever, on Thursday or Friday morning.

Most professors don't fight this dynamic. Some schools do not even schedule Friday classes. Some of this I blame on ESPN, which loves weeknight football games that totally disrupt campus rhythms at large universities.

OK, maybe I'm over-the-top here, but I do think fewer, but longer, class meetings work best. But not on Friday. After we set sail in my courses, I figured to gerrymander a bit.

One possibility was to turn Friday into meeting with students on an individual basis. Another was to make it a clinic day for the writing class, requiring each student to spend at least an hour—at the time of his or her choosing—in a lab I supervised. Long day for me, but no lecture to prepare and I get to better understand a student's needs.

The writing class was easy. I assigned, they wrote and turned it in on time. I graded. Like the Nike advertisement said, my philosophy was simple: "Just do it."

Oh, and while you're at it class, heed novelist Elmore Leonard's advice on writing: "Try to leave out the parts that readers tend to skip."

My other course, Shakespeare, was more daunting. I'd sat through several boring classes on the subject in college myself, so I knew the drill.

To ease everyone into the course, I planned to show films adapted from the plays as well as a documentary on the Bard. But I would delay reading plays in their entirety.

Instead, we'd tackle famous lines and their meaning in modern society. Or, as a golfing buddy explained, have them practice putting before going to the range to hit long drives.

Then, I'd divide them into teams to tackle an individual play and give reports to the class. I figured a scoring system to accumulate points and keep standings.

Naturally, there was a big rush to sign up for Romeo & Juliet once I described it as the story of two teenagers with runaway hormones.

I also figured to add some technology wrinkles, with each team responsible for administering Facebook pages on their plays. Would this generate interest in Shakespeare, a subject that generally gets yawns among undergrads?

We'd see. First, I had to disguise some of these twists on my syllabus. Shackelford wanted to inspect my plans.

After all, I was a newcomer and, as he frequently liked to remind me, "We at Harrison College do not like to deviate our *pedagogical* approach."

39

Making the rounds

BILLY JACK ATTACKED his first season like it was the Normandy invasion, employing marketing tricks he learned during coaching stops.

"If we're going to be big time, we act like it," he said.

This included pressuring the school's sleepy PR department to generate preseason news releases on team prospects, a look at the upcoming schedule, and profiles on top returning players as well as the new coaches.

The Mesquite PR director, who saw Billy Jack as some sort of tornado whipping in from the prairie, informed the coach he did not have a sports information director. He was short-handed.

No problem, said Billy Jack. He'd write the releases himself. Provided pictures, too. Later, a news story tracking system used by the school found no traces of his releases being used in any medium. None. Nada.

Frustrating, but not fatal.

Interviews of players on the local radio station (AM 1600) were arranged by the coach. Once the season started, there also would be his own Sunday coach's show, Buckaroo Basketball Bits.

The radio station owner, Mort Bellew, was skeptical at first. Basketball? A coach's show? This was a first.

Mort became more interested when Billy Jack provided advertisers for the show, including the Beaver Motel, a farm implement dealership, and a feed store.

Interestingly, none of the advertisers had competition within 100 miles. They did it because their sponsorship package included free tickets—to Mesquite rodeo.

A schedule of personal appearances by Billy Jack and Jimmy, which led up to the season opener, were executed. These included church suppers, PTA meetings, American Legion gatherings, two book clubs, a Future Farmers of America club, and county rest home.

Billy Jack dragged the college photographer with him on a visit to the Beaver County Hospital to cheer patients, but this was a complete bust.

There were only three patients in the hospital at the time. One was getting over a severe bout of alcohol poisoning. The second sustained a concussion in a bar fight.

The third? He was recovering from burns after his wife hit him on the head with a frying pan she pulled off the stove—and got charged with spousal abuse.

Each declined to have their picture taken, which, of course, was the purpose of the whole exercise.

Billy Jack left his card with several nurses. He asked them to call him if a better prospect got admitted, someone he could cheer up.

"Preferably a kid," he added. "A cancer patient at any age would work, too."

A run was made at the Amarillo News. This was the regional news source for readers. Several small newspapers, and all the radio and TV stations in the area, routinely stole stories from it.

There were no nibbles in the News beyond a small, two-sentence item a few days following a brief telephone conversation with the sports editor. This appeared at the bottom of the scoreboard page on page three. The tiny headline read, "New Buckaroo in town."

Billy Jack cancelled a press day on the first day of practice allowed by the NCAA (and never mind he already had conducted workouts for two weeks). The only "media" to respond was the eager, new sports editor of the student monthly newspaper, The Mesquite Mosquito.

Perhaps the most successful preseason appearance for Billy Jack was an introduction to the crowd attending the season-opening rodeo for the women's team (the men's season was in Spring).

Several thousand spectators were there. The slick-looking coach got a nice round of applause, especially when he popped into the ring wearing a very large, white cowboy hat.

Too bad he wasn't wearing boots. He stepped in a big pile of horse poop exiting the corral, ruining a new $600 pair of Italian-made Ferragamo loafers.

Yes. The preseason was a learning experience for the eager, ambitious coach. Mostly he learned he wasn't in the big time.

In this community, the men's basketball program likely ranked fifth in popularity behind men's rodeo, women's rodeo, and football at Mesquite and the local Beaver County High School.

At the very best, fifth.

40

Infrastructure 101

ON ONE OF his round-trip commutes early in the Mesquite school year, Billy Jack walked through their condo door in Amarillo and said to Merrilou, "I've got the perfect job for you."

"What?"

"Cheerleading coach. I need somebody to show the Mesquite girls the right way to do it. What to wear. How to conduct themselves. That sort of stuff. You'd be perfect with your experience. Hell, you're overqualified."

Merrilou, growing a bit bored already with Amarillo life, promised to think it over.

Without saying it, the primary concern was how much time she would have to spend in Beaver Junction and the dreadful Beaver Motel. Would she have to stay overnight in that moldy Faculty Frat House?

Or, worse, would she have to commute like her husband?

Give her some time. She'd think it over.

Meanwhile Billy Jack's public relations campaign continued to be less than smashing as it entered a new phase: Internal Infrastructure.

There were lots of things to put in place. First and foremost, he met with as many faculty members as possible. He wanted to get a feel: Who'd be most likely to treat basketball players with less than rigorous standards in the classroom?

Some departments—sciences and math, for instance—weren't worth schmoozing. There were concrete facts to be learned in these subjects. You couldn't get away with bullshitting.

He concentrated on social sciences and courses leading to vocations, sometimes disguised as engineering. Agriculture was good, too, though it might be tough to sell to his city kids.

A few professors bristled at the slightest suggestion of double standards in their classroom. As if they were teaching in the Ivy League, not in the remotest, dustiest possible location in Oklahoma.

There were a few, perhaps out of boredom, who seemed to get it, however.

These teachers would come in handy for second semester, when the balance of the schedule was contested and the Buckaroos would be spending much time on the road and away from campus. He assured everyone there would be rigorous study sessions on these trips.

As far as his own teaching career, Billy Jack figured to offer his course in the second semester as a backup for players in need of a fallback position to cover any slippage in the opening term.

Getting the course he taught approved by the faculty committee on academics—a requirement—was a breeze. He simply Googled up a bunch of authentic-looking syllabi, picked something appropriate, made changes to fit his Mesquite offering, and submitted.

In fact, he was quite proud of the finished product: Introduction to Systems Analysis 101. Since there was no major in sports or recreation, the class would be considered an elective—no prerequisite necessary—to be applied to any major.

He was particularly proud of labeling it "Introductory/101," opening the door for retaining the same students for more of the same in 102, 3, 4, etc., etc., if still was the Buckaroo coach.

When he showed the syllabus to Jimmy before submission, his assistant had a few observations.

"What systems are you going to analyze, Billy?"

"I don't know. I'll figure that out later."

41

The Bard speaks

THE FIRST HARRISON semester got off to a decent start for me in the classroom.

The students were mostly white and middle class. There were 14 in the writing course, 15 in Shakespeare. Mostly they were in their first or second year and from the Midwest.

Some, I would learn, were "first generation," or first in their families to attend college. The minorities were few and predictable: Two blacks, two Hispanics, and one Asian. Total.

Gays? Transgenders? I didn't go there. Don't ask, don't tell, and all that. Anyway, I cared less.

In time the better students rose to the top, of course. There were at least 9-10 who had promise and, at best, seemed interested and did not fall asleep.

Others were works in progress. Naturally there were a few with no clue whatsoever. They did not know why they were in college and neither did I.

I was determined to not make final judgements about my students. A lot can happen between the ages of 18 and 21. Today's mope could become tomorrow's college trustee.

As it turned out, the Preacher's daughter, Kate, was in my writing course. I would never have guessed by her appearance—petite, blondish, and seemingly shy, but very attentive.

Naturally, my pedagogy came into question.

The department chair, Shackelford, who I assumed was spear carrying for Dean Brunk, wanted to know all about this "new technology" I was using in a class devoted to the sacred William Shakespeare.

"Really, Mr. Doyle, I mean Shakespeare on this Twatter thing? Seems like you're stretching things a bit here," he opened with, when I answered his summons.

Great. I was dealing with someone who did not know a Tweet from a Twat.

Politely, I said, "Actually, it's Twitter, Dr. Shackelford."

I went on to explain to the Good Department Chair that we simply were sending out "quotes of the day" from Shakespeare's plays—as long it was 160 characters or shorter.

Stuff like this:

"The course of true love never did run smooth."

"Some are born great, some achieve greatness, and some have greatness thrust upon them."

"All the world's a stage."

"If the music be the food of love play on."

The purpose, I further explained, was to make students and an outside audience aware of how the Bard's work still has many applications in today's society.

But first the student had to prove to me this was the case before I approved his or her Tweet.

Each person was responsible for at least two quotes during the term. One student, who I found to be technically savvy—and there's always one in every class—became my site administrator.

"And people see them how?" Shackelford, now engrossed, wondered. "On this World Wide Web thing? Is this what they call social media?"

"Well, yes, Doctor Shackelford, this is a good example of just that."

"And how many people see this?"

"Well, right now we have a reach of something just under 11,000, but my tekkie student is pretty discouraged. He's taking it as a personal insult if he cannot get us above 20,000 before the term ends."

"Wait! People? Twenty-thousand?

"Yes."

There was a long pause.

Then Shackelford sat back in his chair, took off his glasses, wiped them with a handkerchief, put them back on, and said: "My, my, that is impressive. Carry on, Mr. Doyle. Well done, I must say."

Love to have been a fly on the wall when he reported to Dean Brunk.

42

Raise a glass

WHILE THE CLASSROOM was my primary concern at William H. Harrison College, that first semester proved interesting on additional fronts.

For starters, I finally made it to Whitey's. Not a bad place to hang. Nice mix of locals and a few others connected, one way or another, to the college. Real people, in other words.

It was possible to have a decent conversation, though I was told things could get heated in election seasons.

There was a pool table and—I am not making this up—a genuine, vintage Pac-Man, a video game I loved and figured extinct. There was a row of personalized beer steins behind the bar.

There always seemed to be a card game taking place. Once, I even saw a bridge game being played. In a townie bar!

Adding to the atmosphere: The ceiling was plastered with $1 bills, each boldly signed in red ink by patrons.

"I call it my 'ceiling of fame,'" said Whitey. "Nearly 50 of 'em up there. But I don't let just anybody put up their dollar. A committee has to approve."

And who's the committee? "Me."

Whitey's was in a totally rural location, about 7-8 miles from Harrison.

It was not unusual to see a tractor parked in front. When the breeze was right, all kinds of pungent farm smells were in the air.

Whitey was convinced there was a direct correlation between the intensity of the odor outside and how much alcohol was consumed inside his tavern.

"It's just a theory," he said. "I think people tend to linger inside longer to avoid the smell. Maybe you can find me some scientist at the college to do a study. Maybe publish a paper."

The building sat on a bank of the Tippecanoe River. There was a historic bridge in front of the tavern, but was closed to motorized vehicles ever since a flood weakened its foundation.

Pedestrians were welcome—and safe—to cross. In fact, the bridge was a bigger attraction now that cars, trucks, and tractors could not use it.

"Damnedest thing," Whitey confided one night. "I was ready to retire after that flood. Had a place picked out in Texas and everything. Figured I was done.

"But I'm busier than ever. You can't get in here when the Colts are on TV. Or Indiana or Purdue basketball. Flood put us on the map, I guess."

Once he learned I'd spent my time behind a bar pulling draughts, things opened up for me. He began to think of me as a kind of soulmate, someone who'd shared a foxhole in the front lines.

"I don't get any college profs in here, or maybe they come once and never return," he said. "I do have one or two of the trustees, and a few others pretty well connected around town. Don't forget it's a small town.

"The students don't come here, and that's fine with me. I don't want to get into the fake ID thing. I get a few bikers, but don't let that scare you away."

The Holy Rollers? Nate Stine?

"Yeah, you know the Rollers? Nate? Most are OK. I feel a lot better when Nate's with them. He's The Man, he keeps things in check. At least in here, he does."

Yep, this place would do just fine for an occasional break from academia.

The clincher: Whitey asked me to sign a dollar bill and, pulling out a step ladder, he called for everyone's attention, pasted it with great solemnity to the ceiling and introduced me to his customers.

I was now a member of the Ceiling Club, an alright guy. He told me it was unprecedented someone qualified so quickly, but I was OK. It helped I'd tended bar.

"When you been in the business as long as me," he said, "you learn to separate the bird seed from the bird shit."

High praise, indeed.

There was a small, very small, round of applause after his short speech.

Then, ahem, Whitey noted it was traditional for a newly-confirmed member of his club to buy a round for the house.

"We used to grab the new guy, carry him to the Tippecanoe, and toss him in," he said. "There's a few guys in here right now who had that baptism.

"Once we had a guy damn near drown. We finally fished him ashore a half-mile or so downstream.

"Then we started letting a few women in and, well, that didn't seem right tossin' them in the water. So, what the hell. We just make 'em buy a round now.

"Better for business anyway."

43

Versatility

IF THERE WAS a real coup in Billy Jack's Internal Infrastructure campaign, it was this: He found a way to award scholarships to basketball players that had nothing to do with academics and everything with sports.

This was expressly forbidden by the NCAA at the Division III level. Or, as outlined in one of the association's many manuals:

The students on the intercollegiate teams of Division III member schools come to college for an education and they play for the love of the game. Our student-athletes compete not because they expect a financial reward, but because they are driven to excel. The challenge and commitment to do their best comes from within.

"My plan's brilliant, Jimmy," he said. "It's even better than our revolving backdrops for Skype recruiting. And the best part? We don't even have to do the paperwork."

(This was important. Despite Billy Jack's repeated requests for an upgrade, the closest thing to a basketball office secretary was a part-time student he trusted merely to answer the telephone and take messages.)

His scholarship plan was simple: Basketball players would be awarded Mesquite rodeo scholarships.

This was possible because college rodeo programs were not governed by the NCAA. They could offer scholarships because the sport had its own sanctioning body—the National Collegiate Rodeo Association. Therefore, rodeo was not bound to NCAA rules.

Hank Harkin, the school's rodeo director, balked when Billy Jack first broached the idea.

More important: Branch Wilson, Mesquite's athletic director, was on board with the plan. Anything that made another Buckaroo program succeed was good with him. He had hidden incentive clauses in his contract that would kick in.

Harkin, guarding the rodeo program that he protected like a mother hen, had to be convinced.

The best argument was that basketball, a winter sport, did not compete for attention for rodeo, which was in the fall (women) and spring (men).

Billy Jack chipped in with this: He'd leave spots open in his "Introduction to Systems Analysis" class for any student in rodeo in need of a grade fix to stay eligible.

Finally, Hank was won over with the promise that the additional scholarships would not be deducted from his budget.

"I'll find the money somewhere," said Wilson. "Hell, I got ways of finding money both of you never dreamed of."

Harkin had one final request.

"Just don't make me list these basketball players on any rosters. OK? Going to look pretty goofy to have some 6-foot-10 kid from the inner city of Chicago listed as a bronc rider."

This piece of business taken care of, Billy Jack moved on to another detail: To "thong it" or not to "thong it."

"Absolutely not," said Merrilou, who'd just agreed to become the first cheerleading coach—as far as anyone knew—in Mesquite sports history.

"No. No thongs. You cannot have school cheerleaders jumping around and showing their butt cracks to an audience. Gross. What next? Pole dancing."

Billy Jack quickly realized he was in dangerous territory here. This did not escalate into a real argument, however.

If there was one thing Merrilou considered her area of expertise, it was cheerleading. Two years on the varsity at a major university? One national championship, one second-place in the national cheerleading competition in this time? Puh-leeze.

Nevertheless, Billy Jack regarded basketball the main event of an entertainment package. He'd already arranged for a pep band to play and the Buckaroo mascot to ham it up at home games.

Once, on a recruiting mission, he saw almost the entire home crowd leave at the start of a second half despite a close game. Why?

Because the star attraction of the cheerleading squad, who would go on to become a Miss America, did an impressive—and traditional—handstand routine the entire length of the court during intermission.

The team was lousy, but her performances became legendary. They drew spectators from all over the region. There was no reason to stay after they'd seen her act.

Merrilou also fully understood the importance of turning games into a show, but, in her book, cheerleading was a science. She tried to be patient with her husband.

In the next half-hour's lecture, Billy Jack learned more about the subject than he ever dreamed existed. She covered everything in her tutorial from the length of skirts and material of the outfits to routines and facial expressions.

Only a blackboard and pointer were missing.

"It's OK for them to be a bit suggestive, but don't make it a skin show," said Merrilou. "Don't forget this is Bible-thumping country, Billy. You cannot have the girls jumping up and down for two hours in a thong. You could lose as many fans as you attract."

He was not so sure about that last statement. He didn't argue, though. He was not dumb.

Just having Merrilou on board was good for now. She seemed especially interested to learn there was a national small-college cheerleading competition.

In a few weeks, they'd assemble the squad. She agreed to make selections and would meet regularly with the final squad for the first month or so.

"Then, we'll see how this plays out. Don't expect the Dallas Cowboy cheerleaders."

44

Ceilings

As THE FIRST semester reached its final weeks, President Casey invited our little Band of Six Rookie Teachers for dinner in his home. The president sounded pleased with how we progressed in classrooms. The wine was good, too.

Not to brag, but my report on "Daily Shakespeare Quote" Tweets stole the show, especially when I reported we were up to 16,000 followers. I left out Shackelford's Twats-for-Tweet's comment, however. A future card to play?

When I told everyone the large Twitter following was due to my tech-savvy student, everyone wanted his name. I stalled, said I didn't have it with me. No way was I going to share this kid's skills with colleagues. I was not that dumb. I had more ideas that could use his time and expertise.

The only frowner on this night seemed to be Charley Cunningham, who remained relatively quiet. I knew things were not going that well with his basketball team.

Despite inheriting a squad with three returning starting players, Harrison dropped its opening two games by sizable margins. This included the heavily-attended home opener. We were in Indiana. Expectations were high. Always.

I was spending a fair amount of time in Miller Fieldhouse. When word of my undergraduate playing days became known, I was unanimously elected player/coach of the faculty team that competed against students in intramurals.

This meant I peeked in on a few Colonial practices after my workouts. Charley was trying to make changes in offensive schemes, moving to a very up-tempo attack.

In previous seasons, the traditional plan was to work the ball around with at least five passes before shooting. The strategy was made famous by Bobby Knight at Indiana University, a short drive away.

The change meant players now assumed different roles, always a tough transition for a new coach with inherited athletes. Morale seemed low.

I hoped, dearly, that this inability to come together was not some sort of racial backlash from our all-white team. Charley deserved respect.

After dinner, I expressed these thoughts to Mary Jagger, in sociology and the one with the fine tan lines as we walked back to our apartments. Several days into the term we discovered we lived in the same building. I was on the first floor and she was directly above on the second.

"I find it difficult to believe the adjustment has anything to do with Charley being black," she said. "Good golly. This is the 21st Century, and we're talking basketball here, Flip."

I hoped she was right.

By now, after we kept bumping into each other in our apartment building, Mary had joined me several times for a few beers at Whitey's. She seemed to enjoy the atmosphere very much. She was cheerfully impressed to see my signed $1 bill on the ceiling and the "sanctity" it represented.

I explained the high degree of vetting that went into my selection into the club. Before Whitey would honor anyone with their very own dollar pasted on his ceiling, I pointed out, they had to make a significant contribution to society. Complete BS, of course.

In my case, I explained, Whitey cited me for my time spent battling in the trenches as a fellow bartender and, what the hell, for being a genuinely nice guy. I was the first Harrison faculty member—in his memory—to become a regular at his place.

Mary seemed to be buying this. I was on a roll.

"What about women in the club?" she asked

Well, sure, women were admitted. I pointed out several examples above us.

Then I put my arm around her shoulders as we continued to stare at the ceiling.

"Just think. Someday, Mary," I added, in a serious tone, "you might see your own signed $1 bill up there. But for women to qualify, as I understand it, they have to do something extra special for someone already a member—if you get my drift."

This drew a sharp elbow in the ribs. "Nice try."

In my book, an appreciation for Whitey's was a major hurdle to clear with her. She passed with flying colors. For starters, she held her own at the pool table. I wanted to clear a few more hurdles.

Up to now, we simply had a good time trading war stories about teaching, our own school experiences, and Harrison. Nothing intimate, but it was beginning to feel inevitable.

She seemed genuinely interested in my Chinese teaching and ongoing communication with students and colleagues there, including Jing and her family.

That Jing officially was considered in China a "missing girl," a concept Mary was not aware of, fascinated her.

"The enormity of it just blows me away," she said, after my explanation. "Millions, I mean millions, go unregistered like that."

Likewise, I was impressed with her work in immigration issues, time spent in Mexico, and chronicling relief efforts involving the U.S. border. Her dissertation tracked the plight of three immigrant families, who encountered varying experiences—all horrendous.

As we were deep into conversation and turned up the short sidewalk to our apartment building, she asked: "Do you like Mexican food, the real stuff?

"I spent a lot of time there and I'm decent in the kitchen. If I cooked a meal, would you like to come to my place some night for dinner?"

I wanted to say: Does the bear shit in the woods?

Instead, calmly, I replied: Well, gee, I thought you'd never ask.

"Great. Why don't we make it next Saturday, sort of a celebration before the semester ends and we head off for holiday break."

We walked up the apartment building's front steps to the door.

"There's just one thing," she added.

Whoops, here it comes.

"What's that?"

"I want the name, email address, and phone number for your tekkie-genius student. I need some help in that department. Bring it with you. No tekkie, no dessert."

With that, she winked, grinned, pulled me to her, gave me a great big (first) kiss on the lips, laughed, and dashed up the stairway to her apartment above mine.

"Gotcha," she said over shoulder.

I went to sleep that night staring at the ceiling.

45

Enrollment

IN THE FINAL week of the first semester, my assigned faculty committee—Admissions & Enrollment, or AE as it was known—finally met for the first time.

I was told it was not unusual to go this long without assembling. Some committees waited until Spring. What did I know? I was buried in papers to grade.

Ostensibly, the admissions director, who always was a Harrison College vice-president, chaired the group. This turned out to be a 30ish, energetic go getter, Craig Webster, who was in his second year.

To me, Craig seemed kind of young for the job. Then it dawned on me. He was one of President's Casey's new wave, just like me.

A revolution on other fronts?

Already Craig had increased the size of his staff, lopped off some dead wood, and assigned a permanent rep to work—and live in—Indianapolis.

Our committee trustee was Gil Munson, who looked familiar. Did I see him in Whitey's? Does he have a signed $1 bill on the ceiling?

He was local, unlike some trustees, and a Purdue alum. He used an engineering degree to build one of the biggest construction companies in southern Indiana.

Gil was a generous donor. He was a long-time trustee, past board president, and easily could've slipped into emeritus status. "Hey, I keep coming because it's an excuse to get out of the house," he joked with friends.

Interestingly, I learned Munson said very little during the battle to hire Casey over Brunk. Many who followed the infighting figured he was in the dean's corner, given his long and loyal ties to the school.

When he finally spoke on the matter, others listened. "Change can be good," was all he said on the hiring of a new president. That was enough. He now was regarded as a strong, board ally for Casey.

The staffer was Anne Waller, Dean Brunk's administrative assistant. It was natural to think she was his "eyes and ears" on this committee.

The alumni rep, a member of the alumni board, did not show. Not sure what that was about, but we were told this person, Kathleen Adams, who ran an antique shop in Indianapolis, had a late conflict.

The student? A puffed-up senior whose name slips me. Thankfully. At the very start, he questioned aloud why we did not adhere to Robert's Rules of Order. Later, I learned he was headed for law school. 'Nuff said.

The meeting's agenda was simple. Craig gave us a final report on the year's enrollment numbers—those who showed up and those who bailed. There was a fair amount of slippage, but no panic. The goal was to cut the attrition numbers among those who did enroll.

We were told the new strategies, recruit the hell out of Indy and Louisville, were just starting to show gains. The groundwork was being laid with juniors in high school, which meant real paydays were at least a year off.

"It's one-stop shopping," said Craig. "We can cover more schools with less traveling. This is an area that was slipping before I got here."

Harrison, he announced, also was going to and try to make inroads in foreign markets—namely Asia. The international kids tended to be money in the bank, compared to the loans and grants that propped up most U.S. students.

"President Casey and I plan make a trip this summer to Japan and China," he said, which made my ears perk. "There are several headhunting services that are coordinating the trip, plus we have a few alums there we plan to get involved."

When the meeting closed, I mentioned to Craig that I had some resources that might be helpful in China.

"Well that's good to know, and I'll keep it in mind," he said. "We're going to need all the help we can get on this."

I wasn't sure whether that was a brush-off or not, but I had to get back to grading papers. There was no word on another meeting.

Wait 'til next year?

CHAPTER

46

Looking up

IT FELT WEIRD. I had a date for dinner, but to keep it I just walked up a flight of stairs for my home-cooked, Mexican dinner. This was a first.

Mary, wearing an apron, grabbed the bottle of wine from my hand at the door, signaled where glasses were, and dashed back to the kitchen before I had a chance to say my carefully rehearsed "*buenas noches.*"

Apparently, she was in the middle of major surgery.

I heard the clank of silverware, drawers opening and shutting brusquely, something metallic hit the floor, and all sorts of banging and clanging.

An oven timer started dinging, which caused another flurry and curses when, apparently, she forgot to put on a padded "hot" mitten.

There were several additional verbal outbursts—mostly "damnit" and "shit"—that came from the kitchen. It was hard not to laugh.

"Need some help in there?" I called, just to get a rise.

Her two-word response, translated in any language, was quite emphatic: "Buzz off."

Mary emerged once for a healthy refill of wine, then dashed back into battle.

"I'll be done here in a few minutes," she called from the kitchen. "Just make yourself at home."

My response, "No problem. I just got to the last chapter of *War & Peace.*"

"OK, wise guy. You try this sometime."

As it turned out, the dinner was great—a fire roasted salsa on homemade chips for starters, a spinach salad with a great raspberry vinaigrette, and chicken breast stuffed with green chilis, Fontina cheese and chorizo.

Before starting, there was a toast with margaritas to the close of our first Harrison semester. We continued to sip and refill throughout the meal.

Our tongues got looser.

Mary, it turned out, was from a town called Garden City, a former rail hub in the far southwest corner of Kansas. Her dad was a school superintendent, now retired, and her mother, a teacher, died in a car accident when the kids were young. The other driver, who survived, was drunk. He lived, and never spent a day in jail.

"I've got three older brothers. They were all jocks, football and baseball. Pretty good, too, and smart. Two of them, Terry and Mike, teach and coach in high schools. Pete's a policeman in Kansas City.

"There's a 10-year age span. Our household was kind of unusual. Do the math. Four men, counting Dad, and me. It was a regular Fart Fest most of the time. They were always trying to gross me out. I held my ground.

"My brothers call me 'Leasty' as in 'last but not least.' They're very protective. They scared off a few of my old boyfriends. Probably a good thing. We're very tight. Soooo, watch your step, buddy."

She grinned at the end of that last remark, thank goodness

Mary got her undergrad degree at the University of Colorado in Boulder, where her biggest achievement in four years sounded as if it was learning to ski. Fun school, she said, with no additional details forthcoming.

Her grades were not bad enough to prevent enrollment in graduate school at Arizona State University in Tempe, where she earned a doctorate in sociology. Harrison was her first real teaching job.

It was in Arizona where she became interested in immigration issues. In her first year in the program, she worked one summer in what could be best called "forensic social work."

It was a life-changer.

"I was just low-level that first year, but what we did," she explained, "was identify through DNA the bodies of Latinos who'd died in the desert trying to cross the U.S. border illegally.

"In most cases, they had no identification. They'd been shot, robbed, or been victimized in some way by bad guys they'd paid to guide them across the border. Or, they were on their own and simply got lost. It sounds awful, I know. Their bodies were in the desert left to rot, or eaten by animals.

"Sometimes we'd get whole families who perished. Heartbreaking.

"That first year, I just worked in one of our labs doing clerical stuff. I learned to speak Spanish. Later, I went on some 'collections,' when we'd follow up on reports from border patrols mostly in Arizona. Tough duty.

"As gruesome as it sounds, I felt we were doing something very fulfilling. We were providing closure for relatives. They at least knew the final fate of their loved ones who left.

"I went on a few of those home visits in Mexico, too. I'll never forget responses we got from families. I suppose, in a way, it was like that with families of MIA's in Vietnam."

My basketball days at Lake Forest College? My year for living dangerously as a bartender in a university town? Big deals. If I'd been an All-American and played in the NBA, neither of which was the case, that would've paled after hearing her story.

Actually, Mary was interested to learn I gave up the sport my final year in college to focus on getting into Iowa's MFA writing program.

"I can't write worth diddly," she said. "It was my weakest area throughout school. I've always been jealous of people who are good at it. Maybe you can help me."

Suddenly, my star was rising.

She enjoyed hearing techniques I employed in the classroom, both at Harrison and back in Iowa City in community outreach workshops I taught for non-traditional students—otherwise known as real people.

I told her how I stumbled into writing features for the Iowa City Sentinel. If I got inspired, the editors told me they were open for future work from me on a freelance basis.

There always was a chance anything I wrote could go national, too. My story on the Chinese filmmakers that made USA Today was a big hit with her. "I kind of remember that article," she said. I'm sure she was being polite.

I told her one ambition of mine was to return to China and follow up on that story and write others, like something on the many "missing girls" like Jing stuck in a sort of national limbo.

"It's funny," said Mary. "There's a common thread here. Do you see it?

"The undocumented people who come across the border from Mexico are a real interest to me. Now, I learn this: There are millions of undocumented women in China."

It was a startling connection, really. Maybe 30 seconds of silence passed as we processed it and took another sip of wine.

"Time for a break," said Mary, finally. "I made flan for dessert, but remember the deal."

"What?"

"Your tech-savvy student's ID. I want the name before I forget. I've got some projects in mind. If he makes you look good, I'm figuring he's got to be a genius."

Funny lady. I handed over his name, telephone number, and e-mail address. I wrote them on a slip of paper before I came to dinner.

Then, an important question from me: Where's the bathroom?

"Well," she said, "use the one that's through my bedroom. But now that I know you're a journalist at heart, don't look in my medicine cabinet or drawers. I'll go check the flan."

When I came out the bathroom door, Mary was standing in the bedroom doorway. There was a funny smile on her face.

"Notice anything?" she asked.

"I didn't peek in your drawers. Honest."

"No, no. I mean in this room. Look up, Flip."

Whoa. A single $1 bill with her name in big, red letters on it was pasted on the ceiling over her bed.

She walked over to me, started unbuttoning her blouse on the way, and said: "I think it's time, big guy, you show me what I have to do to get a dollar bill on Whitey's ceiling."

"What about the flan?" I asked—with a smirk.

"We can have it for breakfast," she said.

47

Holiday break

THE HOLIDAY BREAK was nearly three weeks and I fulfilled obligations, including a visit with parents in Chicago, relatives scattered elsewhere in the Midwest, and, of course, a stop at the Airport in Iowa City.

I returned to Harrison College earlier than most faculty. I spent time tidying up final grades for the first semester and completed other required paperwork. I also put in prep time for second semester classes in the Grabbe Library.

In my book, the first term went well. But, being on a one-year contract with no guarantees, I needed another successful semester to stay viable for an extension.

The holiday break was eventful on several fronts.

One distressing note was a text from Jing:

FlipD @jing_chi 21 December 2019
Any new stories for me to read?...Not sure if I can keep using university internet...may have to leave... change in papers or something like that... ☺ ...hope still can text you... father says hi. Hi.

Was Jing's "missing girl" status coming back to haunt her? Had she been caught in some sort of Chinese bureaucratic net?

As far as that goes, I was not sure she knew the whole story herself. Her father probably felt it was not good to be forthcoming with details, preferring to remain in shadows rather than draw attention to his precious daughter.

A bright, young girl who is curious, mature beyond her age, talented, funny and speaks flawless English could get lost in the system? What a waste.

On the home front during break, Charley Cunningham, knowing my basketball background, invited me to accompany his Harrison team on a trip to play in a two-game holiday tournament for small schools in Milwaukee.

Not exactly a surf and turf trip to Florida or Hawaii like many colleges schedule at holiday time, but interesting. The Colonials split their two games, bringing the record to 2-5 at this point in the season. Certainly, I was pleased. The school we beat, Calvin, was one that did not hire me.

My role was to sit on the bench and hand out water bottles and towels during timeouts. Charley did ask me for a few observations about the games.

Also, it gave me an opportunity to observe things off the court, but I kept thoughts to myself. The sluggish start to the season?

Obvious to me was this: Charley's new offense meant players had to share shooting; no longer was the strategy for 1-2 key players to be the destination shooter. I could hear grumbling behind his back.

One player in particular was a hometown high school star in Harrison, Brad Carson. He was the No. 2 scorer the previous year, fully expected to be No. 1 this year, and dogging it—with others taking cues from him.

And Mary's break?

In addition to a return to Garden City, she went to her family's annual ski trip to Steamboat Springs in Colorado. It was a tradition with the Jagger clan, Dad, brothers Terry, Mike and Pete, their three wives, and two toddler nephews.

There was a steady stream of e-mails and texts between us.

There were hints in one message of a sister-in-law being "a little too Republican." The good news was this: Now that they were married, her brothers tended to fart less in her presence.

Then, four days with nothing from her.

My imagination went off the tracks a bit here.

Did some ski instructor make a move on her? Did she reconnect with an old boyfriend? Heck, for all I knew, she was married.

Later, I was totally humbled to get a lengthy e-mail in which she apologized for being out of touch. She had to make a flash trip to Arizona and then Mexico, where internet reception was weak.

Turned out she answered an urgent call for help from her old Arizona State University "forensic social work" colleagues. They got caught short-handed because of the holiday. They needed an experienced, Spanish-speaking team member like her for visits that had to be made to two rural homes in Mexico with no phones.

Sadly, she had to deliver terrible updates on the tragic deaths of family members attempting to cross the border. This was on Dec. 24. Oh, wow.

And what did you do on break, Flip?

Well, gee, saw some basketball games, visited my family, got drunk in the Airport, and spent time in the library.

And Mary?

Oh, not much. Visited friends in Kansas, skied in Colorado, and called on two dirt poor Mexican families on Christmas Eve to inform them their children were dead.

Not ashamed to say: I teared up a bit when I first read the update.

This girl was special.

New Ceiling member

THE START OF the second semester at Harrison was a scramble the first week. Apparently, I had not scared off everyone. My new classes, an advanced writing course and English Literature 101, contained many students from my first term.

Kate McDonald, Nate (The Preacher) Stine's daughter, was among them. She impressed me as an excellent writer and earned an A in the first term. I told her I had specialized projects in mind for her for Round Two. She seemed pleased, eager.

Kate was coming out of her shell. It couldn't be easy to have the leader of a motorcycle gang for a father. They did seem to have a good relationship, however.

"I saw my Dad over break," she said, after that first class. "He told me to tell you: 'Good job and thanks, Pilgrim.' He said you'd know." Then, she smiled.

This new term also came with a set of ground rules from Mary, which she claimed were written in concrete.

Rule 1: No overnights in our building. "We're new here," she said. "I want to avoid gossip. There are too many residents in our building who know us. It wouldn't look good to have them see one of us coming out of the other's door in the morning."

To that, I proposed this: What about overnights elsewhere, say Indianapolis or Louisville? Heck, let's get a tent and go camping.

Answer: We'll see. She was smiling, too, as if that idea never occurred to her.

A crack in the concrete?

Rule 2: Anything "above and beyond," as she described it, had to be confined to weekends. "I'm working on tenure, you're working just to stay afloat," she said. "We could get easily distracted. I could anyway, so let's try to stay calm. Save it for weekends, Flip."

Naturally, I tested my "colleges are the home of the three-day weekend" theory here.

In the end, I won this point: She'd consider, on a case per case basis, Thursday night as the starting point for a weekend.

Another chip falling my way?

"Why don't we go to Whitey's and celebrate our new pact," I said. "I feel like I've been negotiating the Paris Peace Accords here. I could use a beer. Besides, it IS Friday, an official weekend night."

When we walked in the tavern, Whitey lit up like a neon sign. This was our first visit in weeks. Like her previous stops, Mary was a hit—especially with her pool playing.

A called, three-bank shot made by her against one of Nate's Holy Rollers was legendary stuff. This is what came from having three brothers, she said.

While working on our second or fourth beer this Friday night, the lights suddenly dimmed except for one illuminating the center of the ceiling. The music shut off, too.

Whitey came out from the bar. He carried a stepladder and bullhorn.

"Ladies and gentlemen, could I have your undivided attention?" he bellowed. "Tonight, I have the pleasure of introducing Mary Jagger, who earned her way to become our newest member of the Ceiling Club."

With that, he had Mary step forward. She smiled, blushed (never saw that before), half-waved and sat down. Then, with great reverence, Whitey stepped on the ladder to reach up and pasted a $1 bill with her name on it to the ceiling.

There was a big round of applause, during which she leaned over and whispered into my ear not so sweetly: "You asshole. This had to be your idea. If I find out you told him about that dollar over my bed, you can kiss your three-day weekends goodbye."

49

A real jolt

THE FIRST MESQUITE basketball season under new coach William J. Burns, as he listed himself in the program, got off to an auspicious start.

There were maybe 900 spectators in a fieldhouse seating 1,400. This, according to athletic director Branch Wilson, was the largest crowd in memory for a Buckaroo basketball game (though far short of rodeo turnouts).

Billy Jack pushed every button he could to swell the crowd. If anyone bought a ticket, they should be embarrassed. He and Jimmy were everywhere in the week leading up to the game, passing out freebies.

There could not be more than 50 fans who paid to get into the field-house. These people either were the dozen or so who purchased season tickets or came to see the visiting team, Emmanuel Christian College in Kansas.

This being the season opener, the rookie coach wanted to turn things into a real show, keep everyone entertained, and anxious to spread the word.

The Buckaroo mascot, similar in appearance to the old Yosemite Sam cartoon character, greeted fans at the door. He freely handed out complimentary tickets for future games to anyone who made eye contact.

Billy Jack was particularly pleased over the way Merrilou threw herself into her role as cheerleading coach. This became obvious when, on the eve of tryouts, she unpacked a scale, tape measure, and video recorder after they checked into the Beaver Motel.

"Wow, honeybun," he said, "you're taking this serious."

After a series of what turned out to be well-organized tryouts, she whittled her final squad to a dozen girls from the original 30 or so answering the call. Two were put on the "weight list." Lose a few pounds, then we'll talk.

When word got out of her impressive cheerleader background, a half-dozen or so more girls tried—and failed—to crash the action midway in the competition. No way. She ran a tight ship.

Merrilou wanted her squad to look the role, both individually and as a unit. She wanted everyone to be in the range of 5-foot-3 to 5-foot-8. At least three had to be strong enough to anchor multi-layered routines.

EVERYONE had to be capable of handstands and cartwheels.

She also wanted a nice demographic mix, an even distribution of whites (8), African-Americans (2), and Hispanic (2). There would be no men this first year, maybe next season.

"I want sort of a lean, athletic look if I can get it," she told her husband. "Their boobs don't have to be big, but definitely notable."

There were video sessions with "her girls," as she put it. Workouts in the training room were mandatory. They also were handed DVDs and a set of rules and regulations she wanted them to study as well as follow.

No thongs, but there was little left to the imagination.

Unlike Merrilou and the cheerleaders, Billy Jack was not as picky with his first player roster. His recruiting efforts were minimal. There was little time.

A national championship for Mesquite was a three-year plan, at most. With an eye on the prize, he was looking for quick fixes—transfers and playground stars. Screw academics.

Mostly this first squad of Buckaroos was comprised of returnees from the previous squad. Some veterans were curious about the new coach, several were not even aware there *was* a different coach. News traveled slowly in the Panhandle.

There were three new faces recruited from small towns in the region. Better to create a fan base for now, Billy Jack and Jimmy reasoned.

The coach was confident his leadership would produce a decent record the first season. To help, he added several last-minute wallflower programs to the schedule to guarantee wins.

As far as this team was concerned, he felt like telling the players: Save the team picture and put it in the scrapbook. You're not likely be in the picture next season.

Mesquite finished 16-8. The team was second in its league, cracked the nation's top 25 rankings (22d) for small colleges one week, and narrowly missed a chance to play in the NCAAs.

This was not bad and, in fact, the school's best showing in memory among locals.

On the other hand, there were some who maintained the record should've been 17-7, not 16-8—except for one of the most bizarre finishes to a basketball game in NCAA history.

The date was Jan. 29. The Buckaroos played Northeast New Mexico, a traditional, nonconference rival. The contest was in Beaver Junction, where home games were on the campus in Werland Fieldhouse.

The game was a seesaw affair. Mesquite traded leads with the visiting Javalinas over 15 times. The clock ticked off the final 7 seconds with Northeast New Mexico holding the basketball and a one-point lead, 67-66.

Then, the earth moved.

A lazy backcourt pass was intercepted by Mesquite's Clarence White Earth, a full-blooded member of the Oklahoma-based Osage Nation—a tribe described in history books as "uncommonly fierce, courageous, and warlike."

At 6-foot-4, Clarence was a very rangy, spider-like athlete. He was gangly, skinny, and, with long limbs, possessed great leaping ability. He was said to be directly descended from a tribal medicine man with legendary, mystical powers.

Most impressive was this: His ability to defy gravity, hanging in the air an uncommonly long period of time when he leaped. It was as if he had wings.

"I feel the spirit of my ancestors," explained Clarence, not one for conversation.

Billy Jack liked him. He kept him on the roster. He was a local favorite some thought could be an Olympic long jump candidate.

And, headed for that apparent winning basket against Northeast New Mexico on the eventful night, everyone anticipated one of his great, long leaps followed by a stuff shot.

At the Mesquite free throw line, Clarence, holding the basketball high over his head in his right hand, launched himself skyward. The fans poised for the slam dunk, and the Buckaroo bench players popped to their feet.

But midway in the leap, a not-so-funny thing happened: The glass backboard moved two feet to his right with a sudden jolt that shook the fieldhouse. The floor trembled, fieldhouse seats shook, and anyone on their feet stumbled.

Clarence, unable to make a mid-air correction, caught the edge of the backboard with the ball. The glancing impact spun him awkwardly, and sent him tumbling to the floor.

He tried to get up, but the continued trembling of the floor kept knocking him off his feet as it did with others in the fieldhouse.

"Earthquake! Earthquake! Earthquake!" came the shouts.

The lights went out, there was yelling, and confusion. Fans struggled to keep their balance and make their way to the exits. Many tumbled.

Like everyone else, the two policemen on hand for security ran for the exits. Total chaos.

There were two aftershocks, but mild in comparison. The earthquake's initial Richter Scale jolt would be measured at 3.1.

With a thousand or so people lingering outside Werland Fieldhouse, it would be a half-hour or so before power got restored.

Included in this crowd were Buckaroo basketball players—shivering—and clad in warmups. The visiting players immediately were herded onto the team bus by their coach and quickly left.

The building's interior was a mess. The concession area was littered with food and drinks. Pipes in the locker rooms were gushing water.

Aside from the baskets at each end leaning to one side, major structural damage was not immediately evident. Engineers confirmed this news in days to come.

In the middle of this chaos, Billy Jack argued heatedly with game officials in the parking lot: They could not declare Northeast New Mexico the winner, he insisted. There were seconds remaining, and Clarence was headed for an obvious, winning basket.

"What the hell you want us to do, call it 'game suspended, earthquake,'" said the lead referee. "That'll never work, not even in Oklahoma. It's over, coach."

"At least declare it a tie, or a no decision, but you cannot say they won, the coach argued. "Hell, let's replay the game from the start at their place. I'm willing."

The best he could get from the referees: If Billy Jack could get the Javalina coach to agree to some version of replay, they would argue the case with the NCAA. Otherwise, it would go down as a win for the visitors.

Starting the next day at 8 a.m. and for weeks to come, Billy Jack's calls to the Northeast New Mexico coach went unanswered.

Finally, he gave up and accepted the defeat.

50

Bad medicine

THE "EARTHQUAKE GAME," as it became known, was not such a bad thing, admitted Billy Jack as his first school year progressed.

Oklahoma was the earthquake capital of the U.S., of course. In recent years, the state had experienced hundreds of them. No one, however, could recall an athletic event interrupted quite so dramatically.

Naturally he hated the loss—snatched from the jaws of victory—compounded by playing games away the remainder of the season. Repairs would take all summer. He figured his Buckaroos would've been good for two more wins playing at home.

The coach also found it slightly annoying that the Mesquite cheerleaders, fast gaining a word-of-mouth reputation as "entertaining," were invited by hosts to make guest appearances at the rescheduled road games.

On the plus side: Mesquite finally cracked the media barrier. The Amarillo newspaper, plus two TV stations, rushed to the scene within 24 hours to do stories on the "Earthquake Game."

ESPN picked up the story, too. Billy Jack got interviewed. He walked a crew around Werland Fieldhouse, which figured to be ready next season.

He replayed the entire scene and made players—the most articulate whether they played much or not—available for interviews.

There was great buzz on the campus. Even those in the rodeo program were envious.

"But won't this hurt future recruiting?" wondered Jimmy. "Will players be scared to come here?

"Hell, no," said Billy Jack. "If you think about it, it puts us on the map. People at least know where we are. We've had our earthquake. Now the odds are against us having a second one. At least that's what we'll tell recruits.

"And think about this: After we win an NCAA championship, everyone will be more impressed that we overcame a tragedy. This will put us more in demand, a better story."

Short of felony arrests, college coaches welcome any news about their programs.

The most immediate bump—minor, really—was the loss of Clarence White Earth. He quit immediately following his spectacular, mid-air tumble.

"Bad medicine," was his brief explanation.

Billy Jack tried to reason with Clarence. He described the earthquake as simply a freaky occurrence. "Mother Nature playing tricks. It's just part of this climate change thing, or fracking. That's all."

He told Clarence he was considered an important part of the team's future. His teammates needed him. Someday, he told him, he'd look back and be proud he was part of what could be a championship program.

Furthermore, Clarence was part of history. He took the last shot in the Earthquake Game. He would be an inspiration to others, including youth on the Osage reservation.

Billy Jack emptied his entire trick bag trying to convince Clarence to finish the season. All he could get was three more words from his stoic player:

"Bad medicine, coach."

Then, he walked out of the office and never again set foot on the campus.

51

Showdown

THE HARRISON BASKETBALL season skidded to a crashing finish in Charley Cunningham's first season.

Led by star player Brad Carson, or rather his hot-headed father, Brad Sr., a local businessman and city council member, four players quit the team with three weeks remaining on the schedule.

A typical story: Dad thought the new coach did not know what he was doing, especially since the strategy meant his son would have to share the spotlight with teammates.

Making it uglier: Charley, no matter that he had an impeccable re-sume, was African American. Racism?

Indiana has a checkered history in civil liberties. Like many states, it contained unenlightened population pockets still waiting to join the 21st century. The KKK had strong history here.

Charley got through the season, but it was not easy. He filled out his squad with several late invitees. In the last game, he had three bench players. He was down to one after two players fouled out of the contest.

As the season stumbled to an end, several meetings were convened by President Casey to look for solutions. The first was attended by the parents of the players who quit. They demanded a hearing. It was not pretty. They wanted Charley gone.

The president asked me to attend a follow-up, asked for advice, and made it known—personally telephoning the "aggrieved" parties—that he stood 100% behind his coach.

The players who quit, if they wished, could return to the squad next year. This set off much grumbling in the community. "This is like something from that movie, 'Hoosier,'" said Mary.

It was not exactly like Charley could expect a burning cross in his front yard or rocks tossed through windows, but there was palpable tension in the air in the Harrison community.

No telling what some whack-o might think was cute. Charley did receive a few letters that were, shall we say, less than kind. He quit looking at his social media sites.

In one session with me in his tavern, Whitey promised to keep eyes and ears open to anything that could lead to trouble.

"I won't kid you, Flip," he said. "It's Indiana. They love basketball, take it very serious. I've seen people get riled before.

"Maybe this, a black coach, makes it different. I certainly hope not. I'd like to think people here are better than that."

I figured if any overt demonstration of unhappiness occurred, it would be in the final home game. The Colonials were stumbling their way to one of the worst records in school history.

Some negative signs waving in the crowd? Booing the introduction of Charley? Cheering for the visitors by hometown fans? Who knew.

Our coach needed someone in his corner besides colleagues and a handful of students, who, by now, lost interest in the team.

So, imagine my shock when I walked into Miller Fieldhouse 10 minutes before tipoff of that last contest.

There, taking up three solid rows behind Harrison's bench, was Nate Stine and about 50 of his Holy Rollers in all their black leather jacket and red bandana splendor.

It was an obvious, but totally unexpected, show of support for the coach.

They applauded and cheered every good thing that happened to the Colonials, occasionally standing and glaring at Harrison fans too slow—in their estimation—to respond similarly.

God bless the Preacher and his Deacons. After the contest, thankfully a win, we bumped into each other at the exit gate.

Nate slapped me on the back and asked: "How'd we do, Pilgrim? Need help again, just call. Don't be shy. Glad to be of service."

I introduced him to Mary.

Nate wondered out loud what she was doing with such a loser, which drew laughs from everybody but yours truly. They chatted for several minutes, continuing to ignore me.

Finally, we exited. As Nate joined his Deacons, he called over his shoulder: "Say hello to Kate, Pilgrim."

I explained everything to Mary on our walk back to the apartment. I had no idea how he learned of the basketball dilemma. His daughter, Kate? Whitey?

We both agreed his appearance at the game with his crew was a huge act.

"Where do you find these guys, anyway?" she asked. "You're practically a legend at Whitey's. There's more to you than I thought. I like that."

To which I had the perfect answer: It was a weekend night. Time for some "above and beyond."

"Lead the way," she said, grabbing my hand.

52

Going global

"MAYBE IT'S TIME to do something about it?"

Mary was right. It was several weeks with no communication from Jing. Either she lost satellite access, dropped from school, or, worse, her parents moved.

The solution was simple, something I'd been piecing together with Mary's input since the basketball season's colorful conclusion.

It was: Find a way to get Jing enrolled at Harrison and out of harm's way.

Our college did not have many international students, but I knew President Casey was eager in a big way to break into foreign turfs. From my meetings on the Enrollment & Admissions committee, our admissions VP, Craig Webster, was hot for this as well.

China, and its booming economy and insatiable interest in western culture, was a prime target. Many American schools already harvested students there. There was "gold in them thar' hills," too. Foreign students generally—not always—paid their own way, as Craig reminded.

Colleges, no matter what they say, tend to be much warmer toward admitting students who do not need loans. The president and Craig planned a trip in the summer to, hopefully, establish a Harrison footprint abroad.

There were many detailed considerations, not the least of which was expenses and the Immigration & Naturalization Service (INS) stipulations.

In a quick session, I pitched Jing as a perfect prospect—a can't-fail international student who speaks excellent English. She could transfer here for her final years.

Why didn't Harrison pursue her? This could morph into an exchange program, which could put Harrison on the map for additional pay-as-you-go students?

Maybe someday hire her as an admission counselor covering Asia. As an alum, I assured them she'd be an excellent ambassador. I was getting ahead of myself.

"Everything is going global. It's time we joined," said the president. "It can only enrich the campus experience. If we can find good student candidates, I'll find a way to make it happen."

So, with me adding some networking to the mix, my input should aid the president and Craig on their trip this summer. Right?

Well, no.

They had a better idea: Why didn't I go to Xiamen University over upcoming spring break—two weeks away—and establish a beach head for them later in June when they made the trip?

Set up meetings with appropriate contacts, administrators, professors and students. Perhaps everything could lead to a permanent exchange program.

The trip would come out of Craig's budget. His staff would take care of travel details.

Spring break was one week long, but the president assured me I could have a couple extra days if needed. He'd make sure my class was covered, though there'd be serious jet lag at both ends.

"Your friend, Jing, sounds like a perfect candidate for us at this stage," said the president as our meeting broke up. "We have time to get her enrolled for next school year. Then, you'd be here to monitor her progress."

It was not until I exited his office and closed the door that it dawned on me: Next year? I was on a one-year contract.

Did he know something I didn't? Sure hoped so.

53

Liftoffs

DÉJÀ VU ALL over again?

On the last night before spring break began, Mary and I were in my car headed for Chicago and O'Hare Airport.

She was flying to Tempe for volunteer work with her Arizona State buddies. She hoped to tack on a little R & R in the warm sun, maybe a long desert hike in a Maricopa County park preserve.

I was scheduled for the daily United Airline flight to Beijing, where I transferred to Air China for Xiamen. This was the same itinerary I took nearly two years ago to teach at the university.

My Mileage Plus points were piling up.

"This is pretty cool, when you think about it," I said, as we hurtled through the early, dark spring night to Chicago's O'Hare Airport in my battered, but trusty, Hyundai.

"What, Flip?" she answered.

"Well, here we are: Two people on special missions headed for distant ports. This is the stuff of novels."

There must have been a full two minutes of silence.

Finally, from the passenger side, "Could you slow down a bit. Your driving is making me nervous."

So much for my narrative.

The truth was that Mary was in total lockstep with the plan to re-cruit Jing, plus other Chinese students. She was ready to help.

Her past dealings with the INS could be big, which President Casey and Craig quickly acknowledged. Welcome aboard.

"There are shortcuts and tricks with that agency," Mary said. "Lots of loopholes, and I—we in the Arizona State program—used them all. In fact, I've done favors for the INS as well.

"Everyone thinks federal agencies are big bureaucracies full of soul-less people.

"Not true. When you deal with them on a regular basis, you build relationships. There are a lot of helpful, sympathetic employees. You just have to get to know them.

"It helps to smile a lot, too, and occasionally bring doughnuts."

I hoped she was right. In Jing's case, it could get tricky when it came to documentation.

54

Early release

CLANG!!

The steel door slammed shut behind Billy Jack. He stood in a small, well-lit holding area not much larger than a closet and encased in wire mesh.

Then, following five seconds of silence, there was a sharp buzz. The steel door in front of him opened and he stepped through it.

He was greeted by a beefy, scowling man in a Texas Department of Criminal Correction uniform. He was frisked, then led into a room with a half-dozen long rows of tables.

There were chairs on each side, where occupants could face each other and speak over two-foot high glass panels.

There was a large, muscular and smiling African American man seated and waiting for him. He wore dungarees and a blue denim shirt with TDCC stenciled across the back and, in smaller font, over a front pocket.

In his short career, Billy Jack left few stones unturned when it came to recruiting prospects. He chased them everywhere—in remote high school gymnasiums, in restaurant kitchens, on boats, in trucks, on military bases, in bars, and farms.

On one harrowing occasion, he rode in the sidecar of a motorcycle driven by a prospect going 85 MPH on Interstate 10. He couldn't have felt sillier if he'd been wearing a leather helmet with ear flaps and goggles.

But this was a first. Never had he gone inside a prison to recruit, though, God knows, he'd signed players who'd likely end up behind bars at some point.

In this case, the target was Jumbo Jackson.

Jumbo, 22 years old, was 6-foot-7, 235 pounds of finely sculpted muscle (honed from jailhouse weightlifting). Only a few years ago he was a much sought-after, national basketball prospect on a Dallas high school team.

Now, Jumbo was on the backside of a three-year sentence for aggravated assault. He was serving the term in the Cimarron Unit of the state penal system.

This was a facility for low-grade felons. The location was 150 miles from anything but lizards, snakes, coyotes, cacti and, seemingly, as close to the West Texas sun as a human could get.

By most accounts, Jumbo was not a bad kid. Just dumb.

As a senior in high school, with scholarship offers from a dozen major colleges in his pocket, he tagged along one night with buddies who got chased from a convenience store for not paying for candy— only to bump into a police car pulling into the parking lot.

This misdemeanor over a $10 purchase led to Jumbo getting kicked off the team, too late to transfer and be eligible elsewhere in Texas.

A series of additional arrests—petty stuff—soon were added to his sheet. Then, he quit high school and eventually hit the big time with a felony arrest for aggravated assault.

Ordinarily, this might not have rated three years behind bars except the victim was female. Actually, she was his girlfriend.

The judge, a woman, did not have much sympathy for the very large defendant standing before her at the sentencing. Never mind that he came home to find her willingly gratifying two of his best friends—at the same time.

Jumbo dropped off the basketball map, but not Billy Jack's. He kept in-depth files—even of those prospects behind bars—on everyone. He consulted it frequently as he looked to his second Mesquite season.

"You never cease to amaze, bro," said Jimmy, when Billy Jack told him of his intentions to make a run at Jumbo. "Where do you find these guys?"

Jackson was only one of a dozen or so "projects" the coach planned to pursue. All were risks in one fashion or another, but he expected no more than two seasons—at most—from any of them.

Jumbo was at the top of the list. He had been a Top 100 high school prospect by every national rating service. Furthermore, he practiced almost every day during his incarceration.

After their interview, Billy Jack became even more convinced he wanted Jumbo to become a Buckaroo. "He'll fit, and he seemed very humble," the coach reported to Jimmy.

"I know we can make this work. Just think of us as some sort of re-hab service. Hell, we'll look good taking him on."

To get him, Billy Jack did something he hated: He went to his fa-ther-in-law, Big Hal, for a favor.

The convict's release date was too late to enroll for the upcoming season, but, through string-pulling with two members of the Texas prison board who happened to be members of Big Hal's country club, he won an early parole.

This was good, but this was bad: The terms of agreement forbid Jumbo from leaving Texas for 12 months, during which time he was to report regularly to a parole officer.

Billy Jack developed a plan for this, too.

It would be his most daring move as a head coach, more innova-tive—by far—than fake backdrops during teleconferencing and rodeo scholarships for basketball players.

His plan to enroll Jumbo put him on a tightrope that could lead to ruining his career as a coach, maybe worse. He would be committing a felony.

Following his Cimarron prison visit, he became convinced it was worth the gamble. If he won that NCAA championship, that's all that mattered. Nobody really cared what a coach did to get to the top.

CHAPTER

55

The Fab Five

JUMBO JACKSON BECAME the centerpiece of the Mesquite basketball squad Billy Jack assembled for his second season. There were 15 players in all, and each was on a full, or partial, rodeo scholarship.

Kind of funny when you thought about it. Jumbo was listed as a bull rider on the National Collegiate Rodeo Association forms submitted by the school. Others were calf ropers, steer wrestlers, barrel racers, and bareback riders.

There were no scholarships for rodeo clowns, or surely someone would've received one.

Undoubtedly, the players would have been amused by this—especially the city kids—except for one thing. They had not the slightest clue their scholarship money was coming from the rodeo program.

The Mesquite athletic department, showing considerable wisdom, felt the less said about it, the better.

Billy Jack retained five Buckaroos from the previous season, which had more to do with politics than anything else. None figured in the coach's plans.

A few vacancies had to be plugged when several recruits had late changes of heart after they visited the campus, or, in one case, there was an arrest.

Organized tryouts were conducted at the start of the school year, totally illegal according to NCAA rules. This symbolic exercise was to run off unwanted, returning players.

In the end, the coaches realized a few local returnees would be good PR. In fact, they were interested in their grade point averages, which figured to lift the team's overall GPA.

The new Buckaroo nucleus? It was an odd mix that shared one commonality: None came directly from a high school basketball team the previous season. Mostly they were from other colleges and dropped out—or were booted out—for unknown reasons.

Two simply did not attend college after high school, one was a military veteran who served two tours in Afghanistan, and two had general education diplomas (GEDs).

In addition to Jumbo, these four figured to round out the lineup:

Vic Franco, a 6-foot-4 forward from Newark, N.J., and a U.S. Army Special Forces veteran with the two tours in Afghanistan. He enlisted shortly after a high school career in which he started for a state championship team in a highly-competitive region.

Franco was mustered out at Fort Sill, Okla., where Jimmy spotted him playing for the base championship. Married with two kids at age 23, he jumped at the chance for a free college education and the offer, also illegal, of free housing and a job for his wife.

Pete "Gunner" Dantley, a 6-foot-5 forward from Florissant, Mo., and excellent perimeter shooter. He was a walk-on at Missouri, played sparingly in his first season and, in a heated argument over playing time in his second campaign, punched an assistant coach, quit and spent a year playing and working in a St. Louis YMCA.

Ollie Maddox, a 6-foot-9 front court specialist, hailed from East Los Angeles in California, where he played one season for El Camino JC and one season for Long Beach State University.

Inexplicably, he quit Long Beach despite leading the Big West Conference in rebounding and visible tattoos. "Personal issues," was his explanation. Ollie was the silent type.

Oscar Fuentes, a 6-foot-2 guard from El Paso, played for two junior colleges—one in Texas, one in Louisiana—in consecutive seasons and set assist records at both schools.

Perhaps the more noteworthy part of Oscar's college resume was this: He attended no classes at either school, but did not flunk a course. Go figure. He was fluent in Spanish and English, however.

Billy Jack had others in the wings, or "works in progress" as he called them.

They included Luke Hodges, a 7-foot-1 beanpole he spotted in a McDonald's line just off Interstate 90 in Murdo, S.D. The coach was taking a break driving across the state on a scouting trip.

Seeing such a tall person in line before him, he naturally struck up a conversation.

Hodges never played basketball, but luckily it turned out he was a huge rodeo fan. Somewhere between his second and third Big Mac bought by the coach, breaking another NCAA rule, he was ready to sign on the dotted line for Mesquite.

"See, Jimmy, you always want a 7-footer on your team no matter how raw," Billy Jack explained later to his assistant. "We'll work him into some sort of a player. Bulk him up.

"He may not play much, but I guarantee there'll be at least once he'll come in handy just for show purposes. It'll be intimidating for opponents to see him warming up."

56

Bridge building

MY FLIGHTS TO Xiamen worked like clockwork. No delays in Beijing, no typhoons, and no Ling and Liu to greet me. No matter.

I knew the way, or my cab driver did, to the university's campus hotel.

It was mid-day, time to wander the school grounds, watch some pickup basketball games, browse the student art museum, and try to get acclimated to the 12-hour time difference. I was on a tight schedule.

The next day was a meeting with Wang Li, or Bunny. She expected me. Considering my warm exit meeting nearly two years ago, I was hopeful a student exchange could be formalized and equally beneficial for our schools.

From there, I'd do follow-ups with other school administrators— pending her directions. Then, I'd meet with colleagues I befriended while teaching. Lastly, I'd locate Jing to broach the subject of her coming to Harrison the next school year.

Sounded good, eh? It got better. The meeting was a dream. Bunny was anxious to work out an exchange and, without question, had authority to put it in place.

She gladly would meet with my president in June to go over details. As an experienced hand in international education, Bunny was anxious to work with U.S. counterparts.

There were numerous recruiting services that brokered student exchanges—for a price, but she, like President Casey, preferred to do things in a direct, more personal manner.

Our agreement at this point: She would have announcements posted on campus advertising opportunities to study abroad at Harrison. Interested students would be vetted, scheduled, and selected for our school's visiting delegation in June.

"An exchange would be most desirable," she said. "This would be a benefit for both schools. I would like to think that it would be possible in the future to exchange teachers as well."

I was sure the home team back at Harrison would be pleased.

My additional follow-up meetings with Xiamen officials went well. So did one, late night (or was it morning?) session with my former teammates from the faculty basketball team.

There were many toasts. They were impressed with my brush with filmmaker Hu Jun, a household name in China. Everyone wanted to know about Harrison College and my new job.

They were amazed to learn of the relatively small sizes of my classes and, to them, few courses I taught each term. It was not unusual for one Xiamen professor to have 50 in a class and, sometimes, to teach three classes in one term.

How was my old Xiamen faculty basketball team faring? Poorly, as it turned out.

The sport became even more popular in my absence. Student participation almost doubled in that time. Dozens of new teams competed on the campus playgrounds. Several amateur clubs, with sponsors, had been organized.

Enthusiasm got spiked at Xiamen, when the nephew of Yao Ming, the iconic Chinese star now retired from the National Basketball Association, enrolled and was in his second year of studies.

While nowhere near the size (7-foot-6) of his Uncle Yao, he was no runt at 6-foot-11. His games in the intramural league drew big crowds, which accounted for bleachers installed on several courts since my Xiamen playing days.

Skill levels were much higher, something else I could tell as I made my appointed school rounds crisscrossing the campus. It was only a matter of time, I was told, before international scouts would pay visits.

The local franchise in the professional Chinese Basketball Association (CBA), the Fujian Flying Sturgeons, recently signed two university students to developmental contracts. They looked for additional local prospects as well.

But my remaining goal on this trip—locating Jing—did not go well.

A trip to her home revealed no Zhang family. My knocks on neighbor doors got answered only a few times. Mostly, they raised suspicion. Nowhere did I get a clue of her family's new location.

At this point I simply was hopeful the family still was in Xiamen. Of course, that narrowed my hunt down to a mere three million people.

I had two days to locate Jing. I trudged back to my hotel again across the campus, where I stopped to watch a basketball game—when, right before my eyes, it hit me.

There was Zhang Yong, Jing's brother, playing in a contest. He appeared to be at least 4-5 inches taller since that dinner in his house, but there was no mistaking him. He recognized me, too.

After the contest, he hustled over, we shook hands, embraced, and, between my faltering Mandarin and his stumbling English, we conversed.

While the exchanges were not eloquent, I learned what I needed: His family recently moved at the hurried insistence of his parents. They lived in another high rise that dotted Xiamen's dense city skyline, farther from campus but closer to his father's work.

Jing was fine, dropped university classes a term ago, and would be thrilled to see me. She now worked in the tea and coffee shop operated by her mother. He promised to bring her to the playground the next day.

57

Reunited

PROMPTLY AT 2 P.M., Yong and Jing arrived at the basketball courts. When her brother ran off to join his team for a game, she and I retreated not far away to the cafe in the student art gallery, a favorite spot when I taught here.

Jing apologized for disappearing.

The explanation: Not long ago a government census taker appeared at their door, asked questions for his census forms, and, according to her father, appeared to be surprised there was a 20-year daughter in the household.

Her father, Zei, feared this could lead to repercussions and a government official would return. Jing clearly was born when national policy discouraged—or tried to prevent—the birth of females. She was a "missing girl."

Nothing was said by the census taker, but Zei felt it prudent to move his family to stay in front of China's bureaucracy. The "political winds," he said, "can quickly change."

He informed Jing that, for now, it would be best to keep her profile low. This meant drop temporarily from Xiamen University, plus stay off social media for fear of government eavesdropping.

"Quitting school was hard, but at least I had my friends," she said. "But no social media? Killer." We both laughed.

Jing was excited to learn of my new position at Harrison College, though disappointed it meant I was not likely to teach at Xiamen in the immediate future.

Which brought me to my explanation of why I was on campus: To facilitate an exchange program and start lining up students.

"And, Jing, why not you?"

"Me?"

"Your grades are great, and you've been out of school for only a term. I am sure I can make this work."

Her excitement grew.

There had—up to now—not been the slightest bump on her record due to her "missing girls" status. Technically, she was a Xiamen University student simply taking a break for a term. This move would keep her a step ahead of any posse.

In my estimation, she would be perfect for the exchange—a bright, outgoing Chinese student who, in addition to speaking excellent English, was eager to learn first-hand more about the United States. She was a networker.

There would be some additional expense, but basics could be provided by the two schools. In addition, I saw her as a valuable peer leader—and recruiter—with the upcoming, first class of exchange students.

If she simply got a stamp of approval from Xiamen University, and I figured Bunny could make this happen, we could do a quick, end run around Chinese bureaucracy.

We could expedite the process—I hoped— with the INS at our end. That would be Mary's assignment.

We agreed to leave it at this: Enroll in a summer class at Xiamen, register as a candidate for the exchange, and get in line when President Casey came to interview in the summer.

"What about my brother?" she asked.

"No problem, if his grades are up. Heck, from what I saw, he might even be good enough to play basketball for Harrison. We could use help."

We laughed some more, when a lightbulb went off for me.

Why couldn't Yong—who looked to be well over 6-feet tall—play basketball for Harrison?

Why couldn't other Xiamen exchange students, if they were any good, suit up for the Colonials? Why not?

For the next 15 minutes, I talked and Jing listened. It was stream of consciousness, but, in all the verbiage, a plan took shape. I had a little over 24 hours before my departure for O'Hare.

So many stops, so little time.

58

Oh, brother

THE MESQUITE PLAN for Jumbo Jackson was daring, creative, and illegal as hell. No matter on that last point. Billy Jack also figured it was foolproof.

Jumbo moved to Amarillo and was joined by his younger brother, Jimbo Jackson, who came from Dallas specifically to be with him. Together, they established a residence in an apartment on the city's edge.

Jumbo then registered with the local parole board. According to the terms of his early release, he was required to come in for monthly interviews and, of course, not leave Texas.

In addition, his parole officer required regular progress reports by telephone from Jumbo's new employer. The job, arranged by Billy Jack, was working as an assistant to the greenskeeper at the Longhorn Country Club where he and Merrilou now were popular members.

But Jumbo would spend very little time in Amarillo. That's because he enrolled and lived in a dormitory at Mesquite College—just over the border in Oklahoma—registering with Jimbo's identity and arrest-free records.

Meanwhile, Jimbo, under Jumbo's identity, filled the job at the country club. Furthermore, he grew to like it. People were nice to him. He found that he enjoyed working outdoors and, as it turned out, he—a city kid— exhibited a bit of a green thumb.

His boss at the country club was impressed by Jimbo's work ethic and friendliness. He gave nothing but rave reviews to the parole officer, who, with no clue it really was Jimbo and not Jumbo, was confident Jumbo was on his way to becoming a productive citizen.

Once a month, the real Jumbo religiously appeared in Amarillo and went to his personal interview. Thus, the officer, up to his ears in cases— crime being a growth industry in Texas—saw no need to keep a closer eye on than these interviews.

While in Amarillo for the visits, Jumbo collected his mail at the apartment, stayed overnight, and went for dinner with Jimbo. They found it to be great sibling bonding, making up for the interruption caused by Jumbo's incarceration.

In a sort of perverted way, Billy Jack's "rehabilitation program" was more effective than anything the State of Texas could have provided.

It's academic

MESQUITE COLLEGE CLASSES for his new team? Billy Jack had that covered, too, thank you very much.

Every Buckaroo basketball player was enrolled in his Intro to Systems Analysis 101 class. As part of his agreement with the rodeo program, several bull riders and steer wrestlers also got admitted.

Billy Jack surveyed other Mesquite courses that figured to be low-hanging fruit for his players. Among them: Intro to Pottery Making, Agricultural Journalism, Health & Recreation, Dynamics of Physical Fitness, Rodeo History, Music Appreciation, and Nutrition 101.

Even Oscar Fuentes' fluency in Spanish and English got put to work.

The coach, after consulting with the college's language department, arranged for Oscar to get credit for an independent study project. The title: Spanish In Real Life.

In the course, Oscar would write a paper on his semester-long efforts to help a hand-picked group of students learn Spanish outside the classroom without traditional aids.

Naturally, the handpicked students were Buckaroo basketball teammates. But this class was part of a bigger plan for Billy Jack.

"Been thinking about this for a while," he told Jimmy. He wanted to develop a second language for his players to use during games, which could baffle opponents.

Imagine Oscar, his point guard, bringing the basketball up the court in a tight game and calling out: "Dar y seguir *mi derecho*!"

Certainly, this could be more effective than: "Give and go to my right side!"

As a bonus, the Buckaroos would not need an extensive Spanish vocabulary. They needed to learn only enough words and phrases for 10 or so plays to be called sporadically in the foreign language.

"I like this a lot," said Jimmy, when his coach further explained the strategy. "Maybe we can talk the language department into letting Oscar do it again in the second semester, when the season's in full swing."

The coach added, "That's a good thought, and I've got another secret weapon on the academic front."

"What's that?" asked his assistant.

"Distance learning," the coach continued. "Courses on the internet. Schools are hot to get into it these days. Our guys don't even have to attend class! There'll be all kinds of angles for us."

Billy Jack also arranged for two tutors to assist his Buckaroos. One would specialize in term paper writing.

In addition to paying the tutors an hourly wage, he would award bonuses to them on a sliding scale for A's, B's, and individual GPA's in excess of C+. His parting words to the tutors: "Don't bother me with details."

The wheels continued turning. Nothing would be left to chance.

60

Doubling up

BILLY JACK NEVER envisioned Merrilou could get so passionate, which was saying something.

After volunteering to coach Mesquite cheerleaders that first year as some sort of hobby, he saw his bride's enthusiasm grow with each Buckaroo basketball contest.

Now, after re-upping for a second campaign, she was fully committed. No, she was more than simply fully committed. She was hooked.

She spent the summer plotting—and talking about—the next season almost as much as her husband, who tried not to sound bored by her new toy.

Her habit of doodling on paper napkins in restaurants—typically of faces—morphed into diagrams of new routines. One night, she called out loudly in her sleep: "No, no! Your stance stays square. Don't sag to the left!"

If rules held little or no standing in building a Mesquite basketball program, they meant even less to her when it came to cheerleading. In fact, there were no rules as far as anyone knew. There was competition, however. Plenty of that.

The Buckaroo cheerleaders were filmed the final five games of the first season, tapes that she reviewed numerous times over the summer.

Tryouts for the second season would be more thorough, with participants required to show more athleticism.

The squad would be increased to 15 and become coed, with at least three slots going to men. When the final lineup, plus three reserves, was selected, they would attend two pre-season clinics to get ideas for routines and technique.

Oh, and personal appearances. There would be a schedule of community events for her squad to attend to help build a following. Big Hal hired a tekkie to produce a video for promotional purposes.

Billy Jack became annoyed when she scheduled a visit to the Beaver County Hospital and it was a huge hit. She was crashing his turf. He bit his tongue.

Merrilou started too late the previous year to enter competitions, but, now with time and interest to survey the scene, she had a goal: Win the National Collegiate Cheerleading Association (NCCA) championship.

"Wouldn't that be exciting, Honey?" said Merrilou one night as they drove home from dinner at their Amarillo club. "You win the basketball championship and I win the cheerleading championship."

"Yeah, great."

"And I understand that's never happened before—one school winning both titles the same year."

"Yeah, great."

"At little old Mesquite. The Buckaroos. Imagine."

"Yeah, great."

"We could put that place on the map."

"Mmmmmm."

"Wonder if we shouldn't consider a pep band to play at games?"

"Whatever."

61

Technology challenged

THERE ARE MEETINGS and then there are meetings. They're a way of life in academia. I was warned.

No sooner did I return from my hastily-organized spring break in China, still deep into jet lag, and there was Dr. Shackelford at my office door after the first morning class.

"Dean Brunk would like to see you at your earliest convenience," said the English department chair. "I just came from his office."

"What? Do I need a coat and tie?" I asked.

I detected a slight smile on the chair's face.

"No, he might not recognize you," he said, his expression morphing into a quiet laugh as he turned and walked away.

Whoa. The old boy was warming to me.

"I think the subject is of a positive nature," he added, quickly, over his shoulder.

Later that afternoon, Anne Waller, the Dean's administrative aide and fellow Admissions/Enrollment committee member, ushered me into his office.

Brunk continued to read a paper for a few seconds, then put it down, looked up and acknowledged my presence with a slight nod.

"Ah, yes, Mr. Doyle," he said. "Thank you for seeing me on such short notice. First, I have to apologize. This meeting should've taken place a few weeks ago, or at least before Spring break.

"Generally, I do not wait this long on these matters. You are, or have been, a bit of a special case."

Gulp.

"I think I have what you would consider good news," he continued. "We are prepared to extend your position and, in some ways, be inventive at the same time. We are creating an entirely new job description.

"Congratulations on that. In my considerable years here, I do not recall anything similar to this."

Brunk said my title would be Long Term Teaching Professional (LTTP). I was informed this ranked somewhere between Instructor and Assistant Professor.

It would not be in the tenure track, the sacred ground he reserved for PhDs. However, there would be a three-year contract with fair salary raises and full benefits.

"From everything I gather, you are doing a good job," he said. "I am told your background seems to be a nice fit for what Jon has in mind.

"Far be it for me to stand in in the way of *his* progress."

Never, of course, did he ask me if I accepted the offer.

I would, of course. That was a given. If I didn't, Mary would shoot me, drop my body in the Tippecanoe River, and never look back.

"Anne has the paperwork for you on your way out," he added. "Dr. Shackelford obviously remains your immediate superior in the English Department. It's his call on courses and schedules, of course."

Anne had a big smile on her face as I exited his office.

"Nice to know we're not going to lose you on the committee," she said. "This stuff's pretty perfunctory. You can bring it back to me, or take it to HR. Any questions, just e-mail or text me?"

I wondered out loud: "If I have a question for Dean Brunk, could I have his e-mail address? I might see something that I'd like to clarify."

"Oh, well, just email me. I'll relay your query. The Dean doesn't do e-mail or text."

"Doesn't do e-mail?"

"He never learned, so I'm the point person. It hasn't made for too many delays."

As I walked out the door, it occurred to me: The Dean of a fully-accredited college is technology-illiterate.

Meanwhile, my department chair thought Twitter was Twatter.

Higher education? Gotta love it.

62

On a roll

MY NEXT MEETING after getting my good news on a contract was in President Casey's office, where our ad hoc "recruit China" committee—me, Jonathan, admissions director Chris Webster—met for my briefing.

At my suggestion, we were joined by basketball coach Charley Cunningham. I had some added wrinkles to bounce off everyone present.

Before we got started, the president pulled me aside and seemed quite pleased that my meeting with Dean Brunk went well. Then, in what amounted to an "announcement," he informed the group of my new status.

No one saluted. It was a nice feeling, but it felt just as good to get the glowing reactions to my China spadework.

I passed around a note pledging cooperation and greetings from Wang Li, Dean of the university's College of Communication. She assured us large numbers of qualified students would be interested in the exchange.

They were fascinated to learn of her preferred nickname, Bunny. They loved any, and all, gossip.

I explained necessary logistics, showing maps of the Xiamen campus. I described my teaching experiences there and, as best as possible, what to look for in Chinese students.

President Casey, taking notes, agreed to start direct communication with the Dean Bunny. The details of interviews and screening would be handled by Craig. The process figured to be a summer-long exercise.

In June, the contacts and selections—up to a dozen students, if possible—would be made in China by a boots-on-the-ground Harrison delegation. There would be much paperwork, naturally, and details to finalize at our end such as housing, courses, transportation, and, of course, the ever-present INS.

The basic terms were simple: Harrison provided free tuition, room, and board for up to a dozen students for the academic year. Xiamen University would do the same for a like number of Harrison students the subsequent year.

Thus, we had plenty of time to look for Harrison students interested in the exchange. We were confident this would be helped by a positive experience hosting their Chinese counterparts. For me, one thing was unexpected.

The president wanted me to make the trip again in June with Craig and him. That was not mentioned before and, until my meeting with Dean Brunk, I was not sure I would be working at Harrison in June.

Well, what the heck. I wasn't going to turn down a chance to increase my Mileage Plus points.

Oh, and Charley Cunningham? Well, I wanted some input from him in this exchange as well. Wouldn't it be interesting if some of those Chinese transfers just happened to be good at basketball? This took up the last half-hour of our meeting and concluded with everyone smiling.

That night at Whitey's, Mary was totally engrossed with the update.

"You're really on a roll, Flip," she said. "A new three-year contract—a promotion, really—and now spearheading this. Way cool. You should be proud."

I couldn't get her to buy that a Long Term Teaching Professional (LTTP) outranked her status as a non-tenured Assistant Professor.

"Nice try," she said, "but let's not get carried away."

I reminded her that she had a role in all of this. The committee counted on her to smooth wrinkles with U.S. immigration officials. She was happy to be involved.

"Sounds like it is going to be a very busy summer," she said. "We may not see a whole lot of each other."

Solution: Following the end of the current school year and before mid-August, we'd carve out a written-in-stone, week vacation somewhere between my China project and her summer work at Arizona State.

"I've got an idea," said Mary. "Stay loose. I'll keep you posted."

Sounded good to me.

V

Gang's all here

MESQUITE'S SPORTS TEAMS, with the exception of rodeo, competed in the Tri-state Athletic Conference, or TriAC as it was frequently called.

It was an odd collection of schools seemingly with little or nothing in common. For starters, its members were in four states instead of three as indicated by the name: Kansas, Oklahoma, Texas and New Mexico.

Five years ago, the lone school from New Mexico—Las Vegas State in Las Vegas, N.M.—was admitted. It replaced Phillips College in Bartlesville, Okla., a school with close connections to the oil industry that dropped all extracurricular activities following downturns in commercial energy.

After ruling out the Quad State Athletic Conference as a new name, league administrators were in no hurry for a new label. After all, the Big 10 had 14 schools and DePaul University, located in the heart of the Midwest, Chicago, belonged to the Big East Conference.

To their credit, an offer to sell league naming rights to two commercial enterprises, Taco Bell and Lone Star beer, were rejected by TriAC administrators.

Two members were decidedly religious: Baptist College in Hutchison, Kan., and Oklahoma Lutheran in Guymon, Okla. When they met in football, the contest was called the Bible Bowl.

The Bible Bowl contest always started with the host school's chaplain leading spectators in the Lord's Prayer. Players took two knees, no matter if they hadn't been to church in years.

There were two directional schools: Southwestern State in Dodge City, Kan., and Northwestern State in Wichita Falls, Texas. Some found it amusing that Southwestern actually was northwest of Northwestern. With Las Vegas, they were the only public institutions in the conference.

Will Rogers College was in Claremore, Okla., hometown of the famous, legendary entertainer and, appropriately, known for its theatre department. Their nickname was the Lariats.

Will Rogers was the only league member with a hockey program. Will, its namesake, would've found humor in this. College hockey in Oklahoma? Las Vegas had the lone ski program, but at least it was close to Taos.

Mesquite and Longhorn College in Lubbock, Texas, the Buckaroos and Cowboys, were the only members with rodeo programs. They were national powers with one of the great, historic rivalries in all the West.

Buckaroos vs. Cowboys? How could they not be rodeo rivals?

In recent years, Longhorn owned an edge with its deep core of skilled calf ropers and bronco busters leading their stampede. The Buckaroos owned the steer wrestling division, however. Always.

Outside of rodeo, few TriAc teams or athletes enjoyed high-profile glory. Perhaps the most successful was a golfer, Molly Ballen, winner of two tournaments on the Ladies Professional Golf Association tour.

Over the years, baseball players got drafted by big league clubs but none advanced past Class AA in the minors. As far as anyone knew, there never was a TriAC football player drafted by the NFL. Several played in the Arena Indoor League and in a pro league in Italy.

At least a dozen basketball players made big names for themselves in the college ranks, but only after transferring to better-known schools outside the TriAC. Two league alums did play pro—one in Uruguay, the other in Fiji.

Billy Jack knew the history of TriAC athletics better than the members' sports information directors. "Some weird stuff," he said. "You could write a book about this league."

The coach also knew this: Outside of a Northwestern State women's team once making it to the Elite Eight, no other TriAC team ever made noise in NCAA basketball.

He was poised to change this—in only his second season at the Buckaroo helm.

"The more I look at it, this is the season to go all the way," said Billy Jack.

He made the comment after watching his newly-assembled Mesquite squad go through one of its pre-season practices (two weeks before they were allowed according to NCAA rules).

"Agreed," said Jimmy. "Let's face it. How long can we keep these guys together in a place like Beaver Junction? We need to get all we can out of them, like now."

No question about that. None of the newcomers had seen the campus before arriving to enroll.

Their first impressions ranged from big Luke Hodges rushing off to see rodeo workouts to Pete "Gunner" Dantley's outburst, "Are you shitting me? This is it?"

Ollie Maddox was his characteristic, stoic self, though Jimmy noted his ever-present frown seemed go grow a bit deeper, very much resembling a scowl. A new line appeared on the big guy's forehead.

It was difficult to get a read on Oscar Fuentes. He did, however, get excited over his additional role of teaching Spanish to his teammates.

"Wait'll my Mom hears I'm a teacher," he said. "From now on, boys, just call me 'professor.'"

Oscar's enthusiasm grew when Jimmy showed him the classroom in which he'd do some of his lessons. This was a first. In his two previous years at junior colleges, he'd never set foot in a classroom.

His response? "Wow! So, this is what they look like."

Vic Franco, fresh from foxholes in Afghanistan and bunk beds on military bases less than a year ago, was quite content. This was especially true after his young wife and two toddlers moved with him into their rent-free small house two blocks from campus.

Jumbo, the team's centerpiece, was perfectly OK with Mesquite. After all, he'd just spent several years behind bars.

But what would he be called? He was enrolled using his brother Jimbo's identification while Jimbo posed as Jumbo in Amarillo.

Could there be a risk of some spectator or snoopy coach knowing the difference? The name Jimbo could easily be confused for Jumbo, which might spark someone's memory.

Then, on one of his commutes between Beaver Junction and his condo in Texas, it came to Billy Jack in a flash. He'd combine the two names, Jumbo and Jimbo, and simply call him J.J. Perfect.

From now on, the real, basketball-playing Jumbo would be known on campus, and listed in programs and rosters, as J.J. Jackson. This was how he was introduced to teammates and could be hidden from the public eye.

"I like that, coach," he said after a long chat with Billy Jack. "That's what they called me in prison."

64

Chinese takeout

WELL, THERE I was in June back on the Xiamen campus for a second time in less than three months. Jet-lag was my middle name.

President Casey and Chris were experienced travelers and visited China on several occasions. Nevertheless, they were impressed by what they saw.

A high-rise city on the South China sea, weaving in and out of bays, islands, and peninsulas with white sand beaches and palm trees? I dazzled them at every meal with my chopstick dexterity.

"You must really have enjoyed teaching here, Flip," said the president. "It's gorgeous. Not the China we get told about."

Yep. You got it. Don't tell anyone.

Perhaps more impressive: The university's College of Communication, thanks to its dean, Wang (Bunny) Li, was locked and loaded.

"There is so much interest in Western culture and America," said the dean. "This is an important step for Xiamen to be establishing a relationship with a school in the United States. I am confident we will have many applicants."

If she was excited, we were ecstatic. Over 100 Chinese students filled out applications for the exchange. The university narrowed this to 50 legitimate candidates, based on English-language proficiency, academic records, and likelihood to assimilate into foreign campus life.

And height. Don't forget height. I insisted upon this. Not only were lines long in our four days of interviews, they were tall.

You see, thanks to Jing, my co-conspirator, some excellent hoop talent lurked in the ranks of those seeking to be an exchange student. Why not pluck off a few basketball players while we were at it? Charley was all in.

Jing, along with her brother, spent the preceding weeks scouring the playgrounds and campus clubs for quality players interested in competing for an American college.

Why not? Why not import basketball players while we are at it? There was nothing in NCAA rules to prohibit this and, in fact, international students routinely compete in U.S. collegiate sports.

It took little to convince Charley Cunningham.

After his troublesome first season at Harrison, our coach was willing to take a gamble. He played professionally two years in Australia. He was familiar with foreign players in the mix.

Later, after our return to Harrison, he almost fainted learning one of our single-year recruits was Wang Chen. He was the 6-foot-11 nephew of China's iconic 7-foot-6 Yao Ming, former NBA star regarded as his country's greatest player.

Wang was one of 12 Chinese students selected for the initial exchange. The figure was based on our ability to house, feed, and socially absorb them into Harrison College life.

Facility with the English language was important. Wang, not to my surprise, knew the correct pronunciation of every significant player and coach in U.S. basketball, including Duke coach Mike Krzyzewski.

Each student would have both academic and campus social advisers. In addition, an upper-class student of our own—some of whom took Chinese language and cultural courses—would be assigned individually to them.

In the interest of town-gown relations, we also formed an "acclimation" committee in Harrison. They would help familiarize the Chinese with the community and its residents.

This committee was the suggestion of Anne Waller, Dean Brunk's administrative assistant and on our AE committee. She was a Harrison native and alum. As such, Anne knew more about the town than any faculty, who, like many college faculties, rarely mixed with townsfolk.

"You can't get Chinese food here, but I know a lot of people who'd like to get to know these kids," she said.

No doubt this many international students at one time in Harrison would be a novelty. The school was isolated. The last thing we wanted was shopkeepers and patrons freaking out when a half-dozen Chinese— some of them very tall, as it developed—walked into their stores.

Personally, I couldn't wait to see these students strolling the town square, window shopping. A calendar of events was scheduled, including visits to the local schools.

Our 12 visiting students included three sets of siblings. We figured this helped provide a built-in support system. Jing and her brother, Yong, were in this group.

There were four females and eight males, six of whom were eager to play basketball and make names for themselves in the U.S. They planned to report to practices.

And speaking of names, the Chinese identities would be a real challenge for any play-by-play announcers.

In addition to Wang Chen, the next two tallest players were Hu Yang and Long Yang. They were 6-foot-5 and 6-foot-7, respectively. Then came Wang Li and Yang Lu, who were 6-foot-2 apiece. Zhang Yong, 6-foot-4 and Jing's brother rounded out the delegation.

Not to come across crude or narrow here, but I couldn't wait for the first game. If any five of these guys were on the floor at the same time for Harrison, we're talking history of some sort.

Wang passes to Yang and he dishes to Li, who gives it to Lu for the layup? Or was it Lu passing to Li? Either way, wow!

"For sure, this is going to be interesting," agreed Charley.

65

Chicago-bound

JUST LIKE THE big guys, the NCAA tournament format for the small colleges called for a 64-team field. The Final Four would assemble in Chicago to play for the championship in the new Wintrust Arena on the lakefront.

Ordinarily, the championship was not played in major metropolitan markets like Chicago. This season was regarded as an experiment and officials were nervous. The arena gave them a good deal, however.

The TriAC was an anointed conference, its champion getting an automatic berth in the 64-team field for both men and women. On rare occasions, a strong runner-up in the league got an at-large invite.

This was one more reason Billy Jack reasoned it was a good year to go all-out with the material at hand. In his first season, the Buckaroos finished in second place with players who came nowhere near matching the skills of the new personnel in this second campaign.

Furthermore, this looked to be a down year for the TriAC. Eight of the 10 players on the all-conference teams graduated or transferred. "The timing's right," said Billy Jack.

Like any coach interested in building a record, the nonconference schedule was loaded with easy, beatable opponents. Overall records were vital in polls. Nobody cared about strength of schedule. The trick was to make the competition *sound* formidable.

For that, Billy Jack followed two tried and true strategies learned on stops along the coaching trail.

One was to play Catholic schools that were "Saint So-and-So." These were easily confused by fans and pollsters.

Was the St. John on the schedule St. John of New York City, a major college power, or St. John of Montana, which never would be considered a power anywhere?

Following this tact, the Buckaroos would face St. John of South Dakota and St. Mary's in Oklahoma—definitely not St. Mary's of California, a true force in the highly-regarded West Coast Conference.

The other scheduling name game was this: Play teams that were branch schools.

Most good, college sports fans know there is a University of Colorado (Boulder) and Colorado State (Fort Collins), two formidable, major college programs.

But how about Colorado State in Durango, a much lower level program? Yep, it was on his schedule—listed simply as Colorado State. And, of course, Georgetown—of Kentucky, not Washington DC—was slated.

Billy Jack did have one, carefully-picked Division I program on the schedule: Chicago Tech University, which over the years compiled one of the most woeful records in college hoops' top shelf.

The game was quite winnable for the Buckaroos, but there was another motive here. He wanted to take a trip to Chicago as a break for his players, most of whom were from large cities.

Then, while there, he wanted to show his Buckaroos the Wintrust Arena, site of the Final Four. "Good way to whet appetites," he told Merrilou.

It would be costly on several fronts.

Unlike Mesquite's other road trips, his wife immediately made plans to accompany the team. She had heard much about the shopping in Chicago on the Magnificent Mile.

Her parents, Big Hal and Ruthie, planned to join the team, too. It would be the first time they would see the Buckaroos in action, Chicago being a more suitable game site than Beaver Junction.

In the end, this would be the least of Billy Jack's worries that would come from the Windy City trip in his second season.

66

Side trip

RIIIIIIIIIIIIIING!

This was supposed to be a day I could sleep late after going non-stop with China most of the summer.

Riiiiiiiiiiiiiiiing!

Hey, I was back in Harrison and recovering from what seemed to be perpetual jet lag.

But no.

"Wake up, Mr. Long Term Teaching Professional. Have I got a plan for us, Sleepy Head!"

Mary, annoyingly a cheerful early riser, called from Tempe in Arizona.

There was a three-hour time difference in the summer, which meant it was 6 a.m. in Arizona.

"This better be good. What?"

"Just get down here. Something's come up I know you'll like. I want it to be a surprise. It's Tuesday, but you have to be here by Thursday."

The first day of classes was over a month away. It was time to relax, but whitewater rafting?

That was the "plan," which I soon learned after arriving at Phoenix's Sky Harbor airport. And not just any whitewater rafting: Seven days and six nights on the Colorado River through the Grand Canyon.

"You'll love it," she said. "Wasn't sure I could make it happen. One of the chaperones dropped out at the last minute, so we had room for you."

Chaperones? Gee, thanks.

She was in Arizona for the summer to lend a hand with her forensic social work buddies at Arizona State. Mary's second love was volunteering at Pima House in central Phoenix.

"It's an orphanage; no other way to describe it," she said. "Pima provides a home, then enrolls the kids in schools that fit their needs—mostly Catholic, of course. Another is a terrific public charter school called Create Academy.

"See, the house provides transportation, clothing, meals, tutoring, whatever. Then in the summer, we find other programs to keeps 'em busy."

She became acquainted through her Arizona State project, which sometimes placed kids at the facility. She liked to pitch in and help in the summer, when regular staff took breaks and vacations.

"Really tough stuff, kind of a last resort for the residents," she said. "In some cases, these are kids we find wandering alone in the desert. They'd been abandoned or maybe their parents died trying to cross the border.

"Sometimes kids just show up at the door, dropped off by someone. Mostly young, overwhelmed moms."

Pima houses 75 residents, all with Hispanic backgrounds. They ranged from kindergarten to high school. It was run by the Catholic Church's Vincentian Order.

The Grand Canyon excursion, a first for Pima, was a reward for 12 residents who scored the highest grades for the last school year. There was hope the outing could become an annual reward if sponsors could be found.

In addition to Mary and I, Jim and Raymond, two Maricopa County sheriff's deputies, made the trip. They were regular volunteers. They also helped with all matters that kept students safe and off INS radar.

One, Raymond, was a Pima alum.

Our group was spread across two pontoons, each operated by a certified guide and assistant with permits to operate in the Grand Canyon.

Food, tents, and sleeping bags were provided. Our tents were large enough for four occupants apiece, thus one chaperone and three students per domicile. I got Rodrigo, Roberto, and Juan.

What a rush.

The scenery was spectacular. The Colorado River was not really that perilous, especially in our large craft. No one fell off a raft. If they did, they would've froze before drowning. The water, runoff from snow-capped mountains, was very, very cold.

At night, the air was warm, dry, and so comfortable we allowed several kids to sleep outside their tents.

The scariest part? A rattlesnake we spotted one day on a lunch break on a sandy shore. Fearless Mary almost fainted, something I figured to remind her of later. No one slept outside for the remainder of the trip.

One evening, we heard noises that sounded as if two, large furry animals—Coyotes? Bobcats? Wolves?—were locked angrily in some sort of territorial dispute.

The kids were great, inquisitive, polite and, in a few cases, a bit shy at first. To them, the outdoors was regarded as a challenging, deadly wasteland to be crossed and not a playground. I could see excitement and confidence in their eyes grow every day we progressed through the canyon.

By the end of the trip, we were like family with lots of hugging and promises to stay in touch. We exchanged email addresses.

"Our oldest students, like Rodrigo and Roberto, will be going into senior years in August," said Mary, on our way later to the airport. "This will be interesting. We want to get them placed in colleges and trade schools.

"I'm guessing Arizona State will be a landing spot for most of them. Maybe one of the Maricopa County Community Colleges. That way they can be monitored closely.

"I'd like for Pima House to look at some different places, though. Maybe a small, private college farther away, someplace where the kids can get more attention. Like southern Indiana. Any ideas, Flip?"

She smiled.

What a hustler. We had Harrison College poised to take its first great leap forward—China—and already she was looking ahead to the next one, Mexico.

67

Stop the presses

BILLY JACK WANTED to turn his second season's first *official* Mesquite basketball practice, as dictated on the NCAA calendar, into a "press day." Hey, that's the way the big boys do it.

A media day for a sports team in Beaver Junction?

Where the only newspaper was a semi-weekly, *The Pioneer,* and the lone radio station, KBJ-AM/FM, got its sports news from reading *The Pioneer?*

No one at Mesquite, including those in the rodeo program, could remember such an occurrence. In fact, they could not recall anyone in the media—outside of *Rodeo News Monthly*—coming to the campus.

When Billy Jack broached the idea with his athletic director, Branch Wilson, the response was immediate. "You want to do what?"

The school simply was too far and too remote from media outlets, Wilson pointed out. "Who'd come?"

So, there was a compromise. The Buckaroos would make a "happening" of a full-scale, dress rehearsal inter-squad game on the first official day for workouts.

Merrilou's cheerleaders would perform and Bucky Buckaroo, the team mascot, would debut. The newly-organized pep band, The Tumbleweeds, also would perform.

To guarantee a crowd, no admission was charged. The scrimmage would double as a barbeque. Ribs, fries, and soft drinks would be served at no charge an hour before tipoff.

When it comes to luring a crowd, free food always is good.

This would be the first event in Werland Fieldhouse since the earthquake, so it also could be billed as a "Grand Opening" or "Open House." Take your pick. Spectators would be given tours—if they could pull themselves away from eating.

"I like that a lot," said Wilson. "On the other hand, what if the game's so sloppy it's a turnoff for the season? It is the first day of practice, after all. Kind of a gamble, if you ask me."

Gamble? That was the last thing the coach considered a problem.

Unknown to Wilson, his Buckaroos had been quietly practicing since the start of classes. The season opener was weeks away. His players were getting bored. This exhibition gave them something to anticipate.

In fact, up to now the Billy Jack's greatest fear was that some players, weary of being stuck in the middle of nowhere, would quit the program.

J.J. was a captive audience, of course. No problem there.

Vic had a family to consider, so he wasn't going anywhere.

Oscar loved his new role as a Spanish instructor (though his officious enthusiasm was beginning to grate on teammates).

And Luke, who started to show some aptitude for the sport, was more interested in watching rodeo workouts.

Pete Dantley, who had a taste of big time collegiate basketball before Mesquite, and Ollie Maddox, from LA's bright lights, were another story.

They appeared ready to leave after the first week. This was the bush leagues. Mostly they stayed in their rooms and played cards. Occasionally, they went to class.

If he could just get them into the second semester, Billy Jack was confident they'd remain intact for the entire season.

Then, a curious—but familiar—college dynamic emerged: Boy meets girl.

In this case, it was basketball players meet cheerleaders, who practiced in the fieldhouse at the same time as Billy Jack's team.

Merrilou, equally determined to win a national title, spent a busy summer organizing her program.

There were exhaustive tryouts in the first weeks of school. Over 60 students participated. A final squad of 20, 16 females, four males, made the cut.

Her plan called for 12 to cheer at the games, with all 20 rotated into the starting lineup over the season. She wanted to build depth. For home games, those not in the first 12 still would "dress" and have supportive roles like throwing Nerf balls to spectators.

Billy Jack's players couldn't help but notice Merrilou's twice-a-week practice sessions, simultaneous—and adjacent—to their workouts.

Cute, curvy coeds bouncing up and down just a few feet away? Performing all sorts of gyrations, bends, splits, handstands, spins, and other assorted, attention-getting contortions?

In tight, casual outfits? They may not have been wearing thongs, but no question some of the lassies enjoyed providing excellent scenery. To them, it became a bit of a game.

There were times when Billy Jack blew his whistle extra loud to get his squad's attention. Still, he was pleased to see the players—Pete and Ollie included—begin to mix with the cheerleaders after practices.

It was only would be a matter of time, he figured, that pairing off would occur. Hopefully, no one would get knocked up before the season ended and become a distraction.

"This is what I call synergy," Billy Jack said to Jimmy. "If anything keeps our boys from moving on, it'll be a girlfriend."

Then the Buckaroos' saw their status grow with the pre-season, inter-squad exhibition and barbeque. There was a full house, though in all likelihood food was the attraction.

Rather than divide the talent equally among two teams for a competitive exhibition contest, the coach matched his first six players against the roster's bottom half.

It was embarrassing.

When Ollie and JJ weren't going over the scrubs for stuff shots and alley-oop jams, Pete was drilling home wide open 3-pointers and Oscar dribbled around defenders as if they were fence posts.

Even Luke Hodges got into the action.

At 7-foot-1, the tallest basketball player ever to set foot in the field-house, there was much curiosity surrounding him. "Hod-ges! Hod-ges!" and "Luuuke! Luuuke!" came chants from the crowd.

Though still working on fundamentals, namely dribbling and catching passes, the big guy logged a little over 10 minutes of playing time mostly running up and down the court trying to catch up with everyone.

Luke did manage several rebounds that bounced his way. But he also missed his only chance to score on an uncontested layup, which is difficult to do when you are a foot taller than everyone else on the floor.

This also was the perfect opportunity for Oscar to test his "students" and their grasp in Spanish play calling. The first team was leading by 40 points at the time.

But everything went haywire. They flunked. When he yelled for teammates to switch to a man-to-man defense—*"defense de hombre a hombre,"* Ollie interpreted it as "Foul the player with the ball."

Final score: 108-32.

"You kind of ran up the score a bit, didn't you Sweetie?" noted Merrilou, on the post-game drive home to Amarillo.

"I wanted us to leave an impression," explained Billy Jack. "I wanted us to create buzz."

"Well, I think you succeeded."

68

Incoming

OUR HARRISON CARAVAN zipped through the southern Indiana night with purpose. The four college vans were loaded with our Chinese students, a few of whom had to scrunch a bit because of their height.

Several hours earlier a small delegation from the college had greeted their on-time United flight at O'Hare. Their exits through the gates, passports in hand, were seamless. Everyone breathed a big sigh with that.

"A major hurdle cleared," said Mary, expressing it as well as anyone in our group. "The INS can toss curves at the last minute. TSA, too. No fun, believe me."

In addition to Mary and me, Chris Webster and Anne Waller from the AE committee made the Chicago trek. Also with us was a professor from the language department who taught Chinese dialects.

President Casey and Charley Cunningham were not there.

The president was at an alumni event in Denver. Fundraising was his specialty. He figured to meet the students on the campus later in the week.

Charley was another story. As the arrival date neared, he got more and more nervous. He pored over the NCAA athletic regulation book, fearful we could be violating rules with our recruitment of Chinese players.

Ever read the NCAA rulebook? A coach cannot go to the bathroom without breaking a regulation. Charley, fearful of a violation, went back and forth on whether he should go to O'Hare Airport to welcome our newest student-athletes.

"School hasn't started yet, Flip," he said. "I think it's safest to wait until classes start before I have any contact that could be illegal. Give me your early impressions, though, will ya?"

Jing was first through the arrival door, a huge smile on her face. Whether she knew it or not, she was my pick to be a spokesperson for the Xiamen group.

"I cannot believe I am here," she repeated at least a hundred times before the night was over. "This is a big dream for me. This is such a big dream."

There was nonstop chatter in Mandarin in my van—and I presume in the other three vehicles—as we picked our way around the Chicago suburbs on the Tri-State Tollway.

Our visitors could see the brightly-lit, Loop skyline of Chicago in the distance. Little did they know this would be as close to a major city as they would get for weeks.

Harrison, remote and rural in southern Indiana, would be an adjustment. For one thing, the nearest Chinese restaurant was 100 miles away. I checked.

It was fun to listen to the students' chatter in the van as they absorbed the early evening sights outside their windows. There were occasional outbursts of laughter, or awe, when they pointed out things to each other.

These were teenagers in a foreign land. Everything was new and different. The flashy billboards drew special attention. They provided an odd, early view of our American culture, or maybe not.

What did they think when the big, roadside signs whizzed by touting "Coors Light: Official Beer of the Fighting Illini," adult XXX superstores, siren-chasing lawyers, Absolut Vodka, casinos, big box churches, and "Custom air brushing at LA Tan"?

Our lone stop for re-fueling was in a mall on Indianapolis' outskirts, where our troops also used the restroom and got something to eat in a Taco Bell.

Most popular item: Shredded beef tacos (crispy shell).

Total bill: $201.79.

Average cost per order: $9.74

Look on cashier's face serving 12 consecutive Chinese customers: Priceless.

After we arrived at Harrison, I gathered everyone around for a meeting. We were joined by students who would serve as individual hosts. Introductions were made and, as I mingled, it did not appear language was a barrier. Our visitors shifted seamlessly into English.

We handed out dorm assignments and campus maps. We paired the visitors as roommates with each other. Twelve of them—eight males, four females—in six rooms.

My hope: After a first semester of transition and acclimation, there would be switches and U.S. and Chinese students would move in with each other in the second semester.

We turned our new students over to their ambassadors. In the morning, we planned an extensive tour of the campus and town.

I told Mary it seems like I should be saying 'mission accomplished,' or something to that effect, as we walked back to the apartment building. We've covered a lot of ground, or air miles at least, to get to this point.

"Right, but there's a whole school year ahead of us," she pointed out. "Keep your fingers crossed."

I was exhausted. It had been a non-stop "China express" for me all summer.

How tired? When Mary started to hint a bit that we might celebrate with some "above and beyond," I, ever so subtly, changed the subject. That's how tired.

69

Orientation

HARRISON'S OPENING WEEK of classes went smoothly. The Chinese students were enrolled and, from early accounts from faculty peers, they were attentive and quite capable of handling material. In most cases, more so than their American counterparts.

They were scattered in courses among core disciplines. Also, I noted there were at least two in each class, which probably was by their design. Undoubtedly this gave them added confidence to have a familiar face in the room. Team players. Not a bad strategy.

The sciences, technology and math, subjects with universal, objective truths, seemed to be most popular. A few ventured into Western Civilization and assorted American history and political science classes, but all avoided topics such as psychology and philosophy.

My bias could be showing here, but who could blame them?

Curiously, none enrolled in any Chinese language courses—a subject in which they surely would excel. Apparently, they were here for more than grades. They wanted to learn new material. What a concept.

There were three in my writing class. Naturally, Jing was an enrollee. One was a basketball player, Hu Yang, and the other was his roommate, Tang Hong. So I had a Jing, Yang, and Hong. No way I could mispronounce their names.

"Kind of a weird feeling," Jing said, following the first meeting. "I took courses from you at Xiamen, too. This means you've been my professor on two continents. Kate told me to sign up. She has been very helpful."

At my encouragement, Kate McDonald—Nate's daughter—was one of our student hosts. Taking one of my few liberties in this adventure, I made sure she was paired with Jing.

Maybe next year Kate would apply to go to China when it was Harrison's turn to send students to Xiamen. As a junior then, she'd be eligible. She was bright enough, and this year's ambassador experience would help.

Surely Nate would like that. He did say she needed to get out of the house. China might not be what he had in mind, but, for a leader of the Holy Roller motorcycle gang, he was a pretty worldly guy.

Socially, both the college and city of Harrison did not present much of a physical challenge for the Chinese students. Some, like Jing and her brother Zhang, lived in buildings in China with more residents than our college had students (approximately 1,200).

The town (pop. 11,392) had fleeting fascination for them. As far as that went, it held little fascination for most of us on the campus—Whitey's, in my case, the exception.

Tang Hong, the non-athlete in my class, seemed a bit surprised our community did not have an Apple Store, which was high on his U.S. bucket list. We were lucky to have Target.

Not long after classes started, I visited both the Harrison police department and county sheriff's office. I informed them of our dozen new, international students. This was a "happening" for our otherwise quiet, bucolic community in rural, southern Indiana.

All bases needed to be touched and that included checking with law enforcement officials. Mary insisted. She had plenty of experience with foreigners getting rough treatment in the American culture.

"The thing is," she said, "it generally brings out the best or worst in people. You never know which way they'll go. You really need to create awareness with anyone who could be impacted. Gives them greater understanding of the circumstances."

Could we be sure no Rush Limbaugh-leaning wingnut wouldn't freak at the sight of a half-dozen or so very tall Chinese walking toward him on the sidewalk? Maybe do something stupid?

Nate's Holy Rollers, in black leather jackets, bandanas, and pony tails, occasionally riding in formation through town on their Harleys, probably were the most exotic sight seen by townsfolk. If needed, I figured his guys could help in the security department if worse came to worse.

Racial minorities in Harrison?

Well, there was a handful of African Americans, including Charley Cunningham and his family, connected to the school. We also had families named Gomez, Lopez and Alvarez. I checked the phone book.

Harrison County Sheriff Lester "Bernie" Birnbaum, who could've been cast as the sheriff in "Smokey & The Bandit," saw no cause for alarm. The officious, local police chief, Terry Cronin, indicated the same feeling.

"Seeing a bunch of Chinese couldn't be any weirder than Amish going through town on their buggies," said the sheriff. "Never had any problems with them. Can't see it in this case, either."

Bernie was referring to an Amish community several miles from town. This meant horse and buggies, occupied by families in period clothing from the late 1800s, occasionally circling the town square.

Later, I would learn from the town's leading bellwether, Whitey, that a handful of the Chinese came into his tavern one night.

"Seemed like nice kids," he said. "They just had something to eat, didn't try to pull any fake IDs. Didn't need to because they had soft drinks. They were friendly enough. It helped that they spoke good English. It's for sure none of my customers speak Chinese.

"I understand some play basketball. Hell, Flip, if they're any good they could own this town. We're starved for winners here."

Field trips to Indianapolis and Louisville were organized for our new students. These were the closest cities of consequence, unless you counted Evansville.

We figured at some point to make a longer excursion to Chicago, where its Chinatown was the only legitimate concentration of Chinese—and Chinese restaurants—in the Midwest.

Mostly our visiting students could be found in two campus locations when they were not in a class or dormitory room—the Grabbe Library or the Milbert Student Activity Center & Coffee Shop.

In the Milbert, their favorite activities were Ping Pong and a card game popular in China called the "Big Two," not unlike Crazy 8s. It took a few weeks, but gradually it was noticeable that friendships were bridged outside their circle.

Eventually the "Big Two" card games included our own intrigued Harrison kids. The game became so popular that a semester-ending tournament, with prizes, was added to the campus intramural competition.

Something else changed not long into that first semester, too.

70

History lesson

IN RECENT YEARS, the first day of basketball practice went unnoticed on Harrison's campus. The teams were mediocre, and nobody paid attention until the season's opening contest. Sometimes later than that.

A couple days before drills started, Charley needed to talk. He wanted to run some of his plans by me. He had two assistant coaches. I was beginning to feel more and more like a third. Unpaid, too.

Who could blame him for being nervous?

This would be a daring experiment: He was about to coach a college basketball team with six members from China he'd never seen in real competition. This was more than new territory. This was a new universe.

Oh, sure, there were foreign players scattered about the American college ranks. A Nigerian center here, a Croatian forward there. That sort of thing. But these were isolated cases. You never found more than one, maybe two, in the same program.

Ours were tall, of course. Their average height was 6-foot-5. Basketball coaches like tall. This was a step in the right direction toward acceptance.

Their added presence, however, gave Charley a larger-than-normal squad to start preseason drills. In addition to several returning lettermen who stuck around last season when others quit, there were incoming freshmen.

Our small-college ranks do not give athletic scholarships. This meant any student, at least at Harrison, was welcome to try out for the team. The situation was additionally complicated by the Chinese being in school for only one year.

Since our squad now was pushing 20-plus players, cuts would be made. "Not looking forward to that," said Charley. "Just how good are your guys?"

My guys? Truth be told, I'd never seen any of them play. Or, at least I'd never scouted them individually. And, don't forget, we had Yao Ming's nephew in our ranks (though Charley and I decided it was a good idea to keep his DNA quiet for now).

Certainly, I was familiar with the leagues at Xiamen and skills needed to compete. I was confident they could play at our level. If not, cut them. They can live with it. They seemed to be here for an education, too.

Harrison was a member of the Middle America Conference, which occasionally got mistaken for the Mid-American Conference—or Big MAC as it was called in our league.

The other MAC was big time, a Division I league with sprawling, public universities that competed on network television. The members made runs at national titles with All-American athletes who got drafted by professional sports teams.

We weren't big time.

Our league, called the Little MAC (by outsiders), was made up of eight, small liberal arts colleges scattered across Indiana and Ohio. Enrollments ranged from 1,000 to 3,000.

Harrison was a charter member and, founded in 1846, was the league's second oldest school. The oldest, Delaware College in Ohio, founded in 1842, happened to be our bitterest rival.

Our football series, dating to the 1880s, was the oldest continuous collegiate rivalry west of the Appalachians. We had lost in basketball to Delaware College—not to be confused with the University of Delaware—10 consecutive times. They steadfastly held on to their nickname, Indians.

My take on our rivalry: William Henry Harrison, our namesake, originally was a military man famous for warring against Native

Americans. Then, as territorial governor, he screwed the conquered tribes—including the Delaware—out of their land in Ohio and Indiana with bogus treaties.

Harrison vs. Delaware? Maybe the Indians still were looking for revenge. Well, I thought it was kind of a neat narrative.

The first time I told my theory to Mary, she looked at me like I was nuts.

"I'd keep it to yourself," she said.

"You're no fun," I responded.

In NCAA Division III athletics, our conference was well-regarded. Most members had a nice balance between academics and sports. It was not unusual to see our teams ranked high in polls and go far in national competition.

There was an abundance of talented basketball players in Indiana and Ohio. The major schools got the very best and biggest, but, for alert, savvy coaches, there were plenty left for the smaller schools to recruit.

"I know one thing for sure," said Charley, as our meeting ended. "It'll be interesting when we play Delaware this season."

Sure, it always is. Why now?

"You haven't heard? Brad Carson? The kid who torpedoed our season last year? He transferred to Delaware. He'll be playing against us."

Perfect.

71

Your starting lineup?

THE CLASS WAS just dismissed. My cell phone rang.

"Get over here. What are you doing tomorrow afternoon, say about 4 o'clock?"

The caller was Charley Cunningham, obviously ringing me from Miller Fieldhouse during a practice session. In the background, I could hear occasional yelling, a whistle blowing, and the unmistakable squeak of sneakers on a highly-polished floor.

"Speak up, will you? I can barely hear you."

"Just get over here tomorrow. You got to see this to believe it."

Charley's squad was in only its second day of drills. Apparently, already something special was taking place. His voice sounded as if he was trying to stay calm, but with difficulty.

The next day I understood. The Chinese guys looked good. Good? Very, very good.

Heck, they looked great running up and down the court, making pinpoint passes, driving to the hoop with moves that would've faked anyone, or pulling up for 3-point shots that saw nothing but net.

"What do you think?" asked a smiling Charley, who quickly came over when he spotted me sitting in the stands. "I know we're still in the first week, but these guys are something else. I had nooo idea."

Me either. I watched and played in dozens of games in Xiamen. There was no way to truly measure how the skill levels there would play out in the U.S. college ranks.

Quite nicely, it appeared. These guys could play big time basketball, let alone for unknown Harrison.

Not to be a killjoy, I reminded Charley the remainder of the Harrison players on the floor—leftovers from last year—were not exactly the Golden State Warriors.

The player revolt late last season, which saw key players jump ship, left a bare cupboard for this new campaign. There were just three returning letter winners and none started.

Did this contribute to the skills' gap we watched? Obviously, we'd learn just how good these guys were during the season.

"Can I have five Chinese on the floor at one time?" wondered Charley. "Is the school ready for a lineup with two Yang's, a Chen, and a Li and Lu as starters?"

"With a Yong probably first off the bench," I reminded. "Don't forget. There are six."

Of course, a coach is obligated to have his best players in the starting lineup. The opener still was several weeks away. Two days into practices, it was obvious there would be surprises in store for spectators.

"C'mon. We both played basketball at this level," said Charley. "I know this is only practice, but, geez, these kids are better than anything I ever saw in small college competition."

Hard to argue.

Opportunity knocks?

IN ADDITION TO the usual lineup of Little MAC foes, Harrison had an unusually strong—for us—lineup of nonconference contests on the schedule for the new season.

There were two Division II opponents, which figured to be real challenges. But the game everyone was excited about would be against Indiana State, ex-NBA star Larry Bird's old school.

The expected mismatch was set for the Bankers Life Fieldhouse in Indianapolis, the heart of basketball country and, just for good measure, headquarters for the NCAA. The fieldhouse hosted some of the most important, big time basketball competition in the U.S. This is also the home of the Indiana Pacers in the NBA.

Our contest was part of a tradition several decades old in Indiana: Each year the Pacers invite two in-state colleges, one big and one small, to play a preliminary game as a warmup for their game.

Normally it would be unusual for major college teams like Indiana State to agree to play a pipsqueak like us. But the setting was too good to turn down. The contest would get good TV exposure and offered a nice payday.

Over the years, well-known major basketball programs such as Purdue, Notre Dame, Indiana, and Butler found themselves pitted against the likes of DePauw, Wabash, Franklin, and Anderson.

The large schools hated it. They had everything to lose and nothing to gain. But the little guys made it a big deal, typically organizing alumni reunions around it in downtown Indy hotels.

Unofficially, the contest was called the "D & G" game by the local Indianapolis Star, as in David & Goliath. Hey, Indiana loves its hoops.

In all the time it had been played, the big guys never lost to the little guys—though one year, Hanover, a tiny Presbyterian college, scared the bejabbers out of Notre Dame by forcing an overtime before losing.

Our game with Indiana State would be in early January, just before we started Little MAC competition. It would be followed by the Pacers playing the Cleveland Cavaliers, an NBA glamor team sure to draw extra attention.

Little did we know, and no one could have predicted, how important this contest would prove for little Harrison.

Let the games begin

MESQUITE'S OPENER IN Werland Fieldhouse was a breeze, of course.

In putting together what he felt was the perfect schedule, Billy Jack observed a cardinal rule of coaching: Tip off the season at home against a wuss.

In this case: Southwestern Mennonite University in Muleshoe, Texas, or "SMU" as he quickly started referencing it to players.

"You're shittin' me?" was Jimmy's immediate response, when first told. "There's a town called Muleshoe? No way."

As universities go, it was not exactly a sprawling seat of higher education. As far as a university basketball team goes, the visitor might just as well as been a high school.

The game was a rout. Predictably. The halftime score was 53-19. Billy Jack, seeing an opportunity to create some harmony, played reserves almost the entire second half.

The final scoreboard read: Mesquite 104-SMU (he insisted) 47. Undoubtedly there would be someone in the crowd who thought this was the big-time SMU.

More important: Werland was noisy, rowdy, and nearly full of fans. The unveiling of a new costume for Buckaroo Bob, the mascot, was a huge hit. The pep band, The Buckarettes, also had new duds to go with music livelier than anyone could remember.

The cheerleaders. Whew.

Despite one twisted ankle and a few other missteps that only Merrilou detected, they kept spectators in their seats in a second half that produced nothing else compelling on the floor. They might as well been the Rockettes at Radio City Music Hall.

Branch Wilson, in a rare post-game locker room appearance for the athletic director for any of his teams, shook hands enthusiastically with anyone in sight. "Quite a show, yes sir," he repeated. "Quite a show, yes sir."

No question the highlight for Billy Jack occurred just before the halftime buzzer. That's when big Luke Hodges, slowly showing progress in practices (he could dribble now), stepped up for a real crowd-pleaser. Better yet: It came on a play signaled by Oscar in Spanish.

Luke, being the best student among the Buckaroo newcomers, had been quick to grasp the Spanish language, but until now his basketball fundamentals had not matched linguistic abilities.

The sequence occurred with Oscar dribbling the basketball at the top of the free throw circle, when he called out: *"Callejón oop en dos para un gran chico jam."*

(Translation: "Alley oop on two for a jam, big guy.")

Immediately, Luke dashed from 12 feet out on a wing and, grabbing Oscar's perfectly-timed lob pass at the peak of his leap, stuffed it through the hoop.

The crowd went wild. "Luuuuuuke ! Luuuuuuuke !"

It was all Billy Jack could talk about on the long ride afterward to Amarillo, at least until they walked through the door of their home and Merrilou wanted to celebrate with some new cheerleading moves created just for hubbie.

Side trips

THIS WAS MY second year in a Harrison classroom.

After finally catching my breath from what was a nervous first academic year, a non-stop summer, and now the security of a three-year contract, I could relax. A little, anyway.

When you build a comfort zone, you become more confident and patient within it. Observant, too.

Now I could pause, pay attention to surroundings, and absorb. Big things, like horizons, sunsets and change of seasons. Little things, like quietest time for the library or what days the campus coffee shop offered fresh cinnamon scones.

My campus routines were just that: Routines, but the comfortable kind that made me feel secure and like I belonged. Even the faculty meetings were becoming less painful, which was scary.

I made a few trips to Miller Fieldhouse to check on basketball practices, but I wanted to keep my distance from Charley and his team this first semester. Time to concentrate more on my teaching responsibilities.

Besides, I did not need to go any farther than my classroom to get basketball updates. Jing and Hu Yang, a player, were enrolled and doing quite well. They always were eager to chat up news of the day.

I took time to get to know better my fellow Durham Hall cellar-dwelling colleagues. A few of the married couples hosted Mary and me for dinner in their homes.

Additionally, a few of us who were relatively new to Harrison started meeting for a weekly coffee. Two were in their first year, including one, Keith Gibson, in the English department. He would teach courses focusing in 20th Century American literature.

In reading old course catalogs, as far as I could tell, this was the first year the school *acknowledged* 20th Century American literature worthy of a full course. This was another new teaching slot for the school just as mine—writing—had been a groundbreaker.

Furthermore, Gibson was an addition to the English faculty, not a replacement, and this brought the count to eight full-timers in the department. We were on the move.

Why the growth? I detected President Casey's fingerprints all over this. Hard to believe this was anything Dean Brunk swallowed with ease. The overhaul continued.

I also became increasingly aware how gorgeous the Fall season was in southern Indiana. It came a few weeks later than the rest of the Upper Midwest, which was just fine. It lasted later before winter descended, which was even better.

Harrison was an isolated, small school in a small town. But we were on a carpet of thousands of lush acres in rolling hills, heavily-wooded forests, and small streams—and in the Fall, it was stunningly colorful.

I'm not sure if famous painters got to southern Indiana, but there were scenes they could devour. The trees, maple, ash, oak, hickory, and dozens more, provided ceaseless patterns of green, yellow, orange, and brown that appeared to change almost as you blinked.

Seen from an overhead drone, Harrison College fit perfectly into the landscape with its red brick buildings and tall, white steepled chapel. A few older structures had national landmark status and, aesthetically, the campus could match anything in New England.

Mary and I explored the countryside with several car trips. For her, from far western Kansas where a single tree is an occasion, these treks became quite pleasant as well as revelatory.

We found several lonely state parks for our wine-laced picnics. We also discovered numerous statues and plaques honoring local heroes. None were of women, Mary noted each time. "Figures," she would add.

On one longer journey, we made it up to Brown County (or Raintree County, as depicted in the iconic Elizabeth Taylor/Montgomery Clift film of the 1950s). We were too late for the annual Bean Blossom Festival and its wall-to-wall Bluegrass music, but we did catch some smaller concerts.

Mary, a confirmed Mariachi music freak, was lukewarm on Bluegrass.

This was a total surprise. I always associated the twangy banjo rhythms as a rural phenomenon. Nothing was more rural than far western Kansas.

"It's OK, I guess," was her judgement.

I was incredulous. I loved the stuff. Who'll ever forget the "Deliverance" theme music with dueling banjos?

"OK? OK? It's just OK? How can you say that?"

"Well, I won't let it come between us." Then she smiled.

Totally disarming.

Was this getting serious? Gulp.

75

Transitions

NOT LONG AFTER Harrison basketball practices began in mid-October, everyone's attention shifted to men's hoops. By then, it was well known throughout town that something special was taking place on campus.

The occasional foreign student was nothing new to Harrison, but the fact there was a dozen from China attending such a small school were an attention-getter. Additionally, the males were quite tall. This could not be a coincidence.

When word did spread they played hoops, and remember this was Indiana, community curiosity grew and grew.

It was a popular topic with the informal, morning coffee groups that met separately on weekdays in the Burger King on the town's edge, Gwen's Café, and, curiously, in the basement of Bauman men's clothing store.

The nearest Starbucks was more than an hour away.

I gave Whitey periodic updates, which sort of made his saloon a clearing house for information and misinformation. The local semi-weekly newspaper, typically, waited for real games to be played before covering local college sports.

The late-season practices, open to the public, were drawing several hundred spectators in the final weeks. No one could recall this ever happening.

"We ought to charge admission," Charley quipped to me following one session. "Or, at least sell concessions. Egg rolls, maybe."

No, Charley. "We've got to remain perfectly politically correct on this one."

Brad Carson Sr., the father who triggered the revolt that sunk the previous season, attended about a half-dozen sessions. He scowled a lot. I noticed he also jotted notes on a small pad. His son had transferred to Delaware College in Ohio, our biggest conference rival. He would be a starter.

Gil Munson, the Harrison trustee, chair of our A&E committee, and regular card player at Whitey's, also popped up a couple times for practice sessions. "Nice job," was all he said, when we bumped into each other in the lobby.

And then there was Nate (The Preacher) Stein. Accompanied by two fellow Holy Rollers, they never seemed to miss a session.

Nate always wore his best leather jacket, Levi's that were pressed, boots shined, clean do-rag, and his long locks and beard trimmed and neatly coiffed. My guess was that he hoped to bump into his daughter, Kate. I never failed to give him classroom progress reports, which always were good and drew smiles from the big guy.

"Nick and Stump," said Nate with a nod, which passed for a formal introduction of his two fellow Holy Roller buddies following one early practice. "They played in high school. Weren't bad by Indiana standards, which makes them good.

"They're real junkies, basketball junkies I mean," he quickly added. "Once they heard what's going on at the college, they got real curious, like everyone else around here."

Then, lowering his voice almost to a whisper, he said: "You get any problems—you know, security stuff—give me a call. I got your back. The Chinese kids, too."

I knew what he meant, but I did not pursue this. Last season's final home game, when the Holy Rollers showed up in full colors to show support for Charley, still was discussed in Harrison.

But thus far the transition was smooth, according to my sources. The Chinese students, all 12, were at first a bit chagrined over their lusty welcome. Increasingly, they came to understand, and embrace, the atmosphere.

With Jing operating as sort of a social secretary, they made appearances in local schools, churches and civic organizations as positive word of their presence grew. She tagged along to make sure nothing got lost in translation.

Undoubtedly, this was a challenge for her. In the first semester, our foreign transfers lunched with the Moose and Lions clubs, and spoke to the local Girl and Boy Scout troops, a 4-H chapter at the high school, the men's coffee group that met in the Bauman clothing store basement, two church groups. We were working on dates with the Kiwanis, Rotary and local American Legion post.

Bookworms

THE HARRISON MEN'S basketball season opener was eerie. No other way to describe it. Curiosity was peaking.

For starters, every seat in Miller Fieldhouse was filled and another 75 spectators allowed to stand in exit ways. Fire department regulations be damned.

Nate and a full contingent of his leather-clad, head-banned Holy Rollers, acting like bodyguards, parked themselves in rows directly behind our bench. I spotted about a half-dozen fans of obvious Asian descent—Chinese? Japanese? Korean?—sprinkled among faces. This was very unusual.

The visiting opponent, Berea College, always brought nice follow-ings when they played in Miller. Our sports information director, plus several long-time Colonial supporters I queried, could never recall a capacity crowd. Period.

No way the visitors accounted for the turnout, however. Clearly, local curiosity over our Chinese players was bursting at the seams.

What really was spooky was this: While Berea supporters were really into the action, there was little excitement shown by the home crowd. No cowbells ringing. No standing ovations. No razzing the referees.

Oh, the cheerleaders and pep band did their best, but most of Harrison's good plays and baskets were met with appreciative, but polite, applause.

Apparently, our fans weren't quite sure what to think of the school being represented by a squad half-loaded with foreigners.

Or at least that was my take.

"It's like they're here to evaluate, not root for, the home team," said Mary. "Weird, if you ask me."

"This project may take time," was my answer. "They just need to keep beating teams. That's the best way to win everyone over, get some life in the home crowd."

On that count, there was no doubt about a victory against Berea. Final score: 87-61—and this was an opponent considered one of the favorites in its conference.

Harrison was methodical. They ran off a 10-0 burst at the start. Four different players scored for us in that stretch. The visitors never came closer than six points later in the first half.

We owned a distinct height advantage, which meant lots of rebounds and second chances on missed shots. Wang Chen, at 6-foot-11 most likely the tallest person in the county, dominated that category.

Our scoring was balanced. The communication on the floor seemed OK for a first game. We had five players eventually score in double figures, topped by Long Yang's 17 points.

Charley cleared his bench, getting all 12 players into the action. More notable to me was this: Never did he play more than three Chinese players at the same time. There were six on the squad and, no doubt in my mind, they were our best players.

"So, what's the deal on that?" I asked him in the locker room, when it cleared out following the contest.

"It's early in the season," he said. "I want to build balance and depth. Get everyone on the same page."

"Yeah, but you and I know who your top five players are. You never had them all on the floor together."

"You noticed, eh? Well, let's just say I'm saving that. Doing a little PR, easing everyone—and I mean everyone—into this."

"You're not sure Harrison is ready for five Chinese representing the school. And a sixth coming off the bench??

"Hey, Flip, don't forget I was the first Harrison basketball player who was black. They barely were ready for me, and that wasn't long ago. Can you imagine if there'd be five blacks suddenly on the floor then instead of just me? Can it be much different with this?"

Case closed. On the return to the apartment house, Mary made me promise not to meddle. "Drop it, Flip," she said. "He's the coach. It's his program. Would you want him drawing up the syllabus for one of your courses?"

OK, point taken. But it IS sports. Everyone has an opinion. Mine was: Let's get it on, get our best team on the floor, and fans will accept five foreign transfers as starters. If not at first, then it'll come with beating the crap out of everyone.

A week or so later after two additional victories, Hu Yang, the lone Harrison player in my courses, gave me added insight into priorities of our Chinese contingent. He had logged plenty of playing time, but Charley had yet to start him in a contest despite his obvious, overwhelming skills.

"Professor Doyle, may I respectfully speak with you for a few minutes," said Yang, at conclusion of a class. "This is about basketball and our delegation on the team from China. They have asked me to approach you about this important matter."

Ah, here it comes. He and his peers are restless. Thought so. They're tired of collecting so much bench time. He wants advice.

"I wanted to ask about our schedule," he said. "Soon we play many games away from our campus. This means we will be spending nights in other cities. With this travel, we fear we could fall behind in our studies. We wish to find a way we can get additional access to the library."

Let me get this straight. You want to know how to spend more time in the library?

"Yes, we approached the librarian on this important matter. This is the only facility on campus with resources some of us need. We were told if a faculty member was willing to oversee our access, and perhaps assign a trusted upper class monitor to accompany us, we could get into the library two hours before it opens in the morning. This would be 6 o'clock. Perhaps all team members could take part in this as well."

"Yes, well I am sure that can be arranged."

Wonderful. Just wonderful.

Me, a card-carrying professor in higher education charged with intellectually molding young minds and I'm worried whether six athletes are getting enough playing time in their basketball games.

And them, a half-dozen skillful players with unlimited futures in a sport and they're worried about getting more time in the campus library.

77

Fast starters

THE RUNUP FOR Mesquite to the Christmas trip to Chicago, and a date with Chicago Tech of the NCAA Division I ranks? It was an unqualified success. Best in school history.

Following the demolishing of Southern Mennonite University (SMU), Missouri Institute of Theology (MIT), Logan State University (LSU), and University of Southern Colorado (USC) in the openers, the Buckaroos reeled off four more wins without a loss. This was a school record.

The 8-0 basketball mark was a first for the men's program. The Buckaroos crept into the USA Today national rankings, debuting at No. 19 in the Top 20. Another Buckaroo basketball first.

Mesquite was a well-oiled machine.

Pete "Gunner" Dantley, firing away with great accuracy, was the top scorer. He was among NCAA leaders for 3-point shooting.

Oscar was thoroughly into his role as point guard dishing out passes and setting up plays. He was proving to be more and more valuable as Team Linguist, with his growing English-to-Spanish playbook.

J.J. was among the top three nationally in scoring, rebounding, and assists and therein was the problem. While most coaches would be thrilled for a triple crown performer like this on the team, this meant closer scrutiny by scouts and super fans.

Would someone recognize J.J. Jackson was Jumbo Jackson, one of the America's leading high school stars from a few years ago in Texas. And, oh, wasn't he the one who dropped off the radar following some sort of brush with the law? Thought he went to jail?

If anyone cared to dig a little deeper and connect the dots, it would not be difficult to learn he was out on parole—and leaving Texas was a violation of the terms of his release.

This was dangerous territory. An NCAA violation? Hell, this was a felony of the first order. And, with each outstanding performance turned in by the big guy, Billy Jack worried a little more. In Chicago, there might even be media cameras shooting the game.

J.J. was his biggest secret, not even Merrilou knew the facts, and he wanted to keep it that way.

78

AWOL

"SO, COACH, WHAT do you think about my idea? Huh? You think it'll work?"

Oscar Fuentes thought it would be cool to have the Mesquite basketball team visit the National Museum of Mexican Art on the Chicago trip. Located in the city's Pilsen-Hispanic neighborhood, he discovered it was not far from the hotel where the team was staying.

Billy Jack, deep in thought, bluffed it. For the life of him, he could not recall anything his point guard had just proposed. He had enough on his mind. In a few more seconds, the coach remembered.

"Yeah," he answered, in a stalling tactic. "It could work. The schedule's going to be tight. We'll see what we can do."

It was early in the season, but Oscar was fully embracing his role as a Buckaroo team leader. Not only did he repeatedly drill teammates on play-calling in Spanish, he had begun adding tidbits on Mexican culture. As if they were interested.

He was checking out and reading books on a variety of Mexican-American topics from the campus library. He was surprised to learn you could get reading material there for free.

And, in what would've been a stunner to professors who never saw him in their classes at the two junior colleges where he previously was enrolled, he was auditing a Mesquite course on Mexican history. He became more and more absorbed with his heritage.

In fact, Billy Jack grew increasingly concerned Oscar was beginning to spend too much time on school and not enough on basketball. Hence, the team never made it to the Chicago museum.

The Buckaroos were in the Windy City two nights. For four players on the squad, the trip from Amarillo to O'Hare was their first-ever flight. Only one got sick and heaved his cookies into an air bag.

Billy Jack gave Jimmy time off in Chicago, with the exception of the game. This was his assistant coach's home town, where he had plenty of old friendships—mostly female—to renew. He practically sprinted through the airport to a waiting car.

In addition to a practice session in Chicago Tech's facility on the South Side, the coach arranged to watch a DePaul basketball game in the new Wintrust Arena on the first night in town. This was the site for the season's NCAA DIII championships in March, a chance to whet his team's appetite.

Whether Mesquite was inspired or not by the Wintrust visit, the subsequent game against Chicago Tech was a success. The visitors led from start to finish against the Division I foe, despite officiating that gave the home team every break in the book.

The score was 83-78, with J.J. scoring a key basket to put the decision out of reach for Tech in front of about 4,000 fans. Billy Jack was not present to witness the final minutes, having been ejected for too many technical fouls.

Ollie seemed unusually energized, leading the Buckaroos in scoring with a career high 21 points. More than a few times he followed up his baskets with an upraised fist and a big, uncharacteristic smile as he trotted back to play defense.

Furthermore, Oscar added a new play in Spanish to his repertoire when, late in the contest, he called for "*un trampa de medio campo!*"

This was a half-court trap play, which caused Tech to turn the ball over and set up J.J.'s important, clinching basket.

The victory, while sure to give a boost for Mesquite in the ratings, was not quite as big as Billy Jack made it seem to anyone who'd listen.

Tech was in major college ranks with the big boys, but its record was terrible. They had won a mere five games in the past two seasons. Its coach was the university's third in five years. He was in his first season and had inherited a mess.

But a win's a win. The contest, fortuitously scheduled two days after Christmas, was played with little else taking place in Chicago sports. It drew a headlined story and a photo in the local Sun-Times newspaper, two paragraphs in a Tribune college roundup, got mentioned by three local TV stations, and video footage was shown on a local sports-only TV cable outlet.

Also, playing against a Division I team (never mind how terrible) guaranteed the AP wire service made it part of its roundup that went to every newspaper in the U.S. This produced a first: The Oklahoma City Tribune carried a short story—after all, Mesquite was in the same state.

The trip proved expensive, however.

For one thing, Merrilou and her mother, Ruthie, shopped up a storm on Chicago's Magnificent Mile on Michigan Avenue. This wasn't Amarillo, after all. The stores were holding post-Christmas sales—but that did not make things cheap.

Big Hal attended the games with his wife and daughter. Mostly he was absent meeting with business partners. It would be a month before the credit card bills rolled in and he realized the trip's true cost.

The real shock for Billy Jack came in the hotel lobby, when the team gathered for the bus ride to O'Hare Airport for the return trip home. He was short one player. Ollie did not show.

"I don't know, coach," said Spider Johnson, a reserve player and roommate on the trip. "I saw him talkin' to some dude in the lobby when we got back from the game. Said he'd be right up. I just hit the rack and went to sleep."

Frantic calls to Ollie's cell went unanswered. With or without him, the bus had to leave. There would be no missing the flight. This was embarrassing. In all the stops on his coaching trail, Billy Jack never lost a player. No small accomplishment, considering some players could barely read or write.

What to do? Was there a connection to Ollie's uncharacteristic exuberance in the game?

"Jimmy, I want you to stay back and look for him," the coach told his assistant. "His stuff's still in the room, and you've got his phone number. Don't call the police. We don't want publicity. He'll show up. Keep in touch."

With that, the best Billy Jack could do was head for the airport with his squad—and hope for the best.

Jimmy, of course, was happy to spend a few extra days on beloved home turf rather than return to his "Faculty Frat House" apartment in Beaver Junction.

The first thing he did was re-book his motel room. The second? A round of calls was in order to additional, old girlfriends he failed to contact the previous two days in Chicago.

79

Family reunion

HARRISON'S BASKETBALL TEAM stumbled into Christmas break with seven wins in as many games. Undefeated, though not especially pretty.

With Charley continuing to mix and match lineups, but refraining from having the five most talented players—all Chinese—on the floor at the same time, the Colonials won on individual talent alone.

There was no cohesion and numerous turnovers. In the process, he lost one player—Zhang Yong, Jing's brother, who twisted a knee in the sixth game. The early diagnosis was not good. Cartilage.

If he was lost for the season, this put Harrison down to five Chinese players. Zhang's fallback position was this: He still was a student at a U.S. college, which was more important to him in the first place.

Or, as Jing put it: "He never thought he would get to visit America. Do not feel sorry for him. He'll get better and play again someday. There is plenty for him to do without basketball."

Two of those seven victories came against opponents clearly inferior to Harrison and, nevertheless, those games went into overtimes. Both decisions were narrowly won when Wang Chen, our 6-foot-11 center, took charge and simply overpowered defenders a half-foot shorter.

Chen, increasingly, was the go-to guy. His ballhandling skills were brilliant for someone so tall. He was good enough to be a top drawer, major college player.

But Yao Ming's nephew or not, it seemed unfair to me that Harrison grew to depend on him with so much talent available from the China connection. Mold them into one unit, pound the crap out of teams.

Over the holiday break, Harrison's schedule included a four-team tournament in Louisville. We played Wittenberg and then either the winner or loser of Roanoke vs. Allegheny, depending on the outcome.

I longed to get in my two cents' worth with Charley before these games. But I put myself on hold. Instead, I accepted an offer I could not refuse.

Mary invited me to join her on the annual Jagger Family Ski Junket in Steamboat Springs. "It's time," she said.

"For what?" I replied.

"For you to meet my family."

"Oh."

"You do ski, don't you?"

"Not exactly."

"Fine. You can take lessons on the Bunny Trail."

This did not sound encouraging.

Steamboat Springs is in far northern Colorado, very secluded in the Rocky Mountains and not far from Wyoming.

As I understood it, Steamboat is a full-scale resort community that swells in population in the winter. Because of excellent trails, and perhaps owing to the isolation, it attracts mostly hard-core, accomplished skiers.

In other words, not me. But I was game.

The Jaggers had been coming here for years. It was a favorite spot of Mary's mother before she was killed in the car accident nearly 25 years ago. Thus, there was a strong sentimental attachment for the family. They had a standing reservation every year in the same condo complex.

We decided to drive to Colorado. Mary gave me complete briefings on her father, brothers, sisters-in-law, and nieces (2) and nephew as we sped westward on Interstate 70.

Rowdy? Hearty? Robust? She assured me I'd fare well. It was an advantage, she said, that I'd been a jock—though it was quickly amended that this made no difference to her.

Pete, the Dad, was a retired school administrator and he'd seen it all. He volunteered two days a week at a food bank in Garden City, Kan., where for 30-plus years he continued to live in the same house. Occasionally, he taught a course at the local community college.

"My brothers and I kind of think he has a lady friend," she said, "but he's too embarrassed to mention it. Probably thinks it'll upset us, which it won't. So, it's kind of a don't ask, don't tell situation until he's ready to come out of the closet, or whatever you want to call it."

Her brothers—Pete Jr. (nicknamed Re-Pete), Terry, Mike—sounded like good guys. They were accomplished athletes, got degrees, and were gainfully employed as high school coaches except Pete, who was a detective in the Kansas City police department.

"You'll like them," she said. "They're very insightful guys. Nobody voted for Trump, if that worries you. Their kids are adorable. I love being called Aunt Mary. From what I've told them, they think you're a good guy."

Really?

"Yeah, well, I stretched it a bit. Don't get puffed up."

The week would not be completely stress free, however. One brother, Terry, and his wife just separated and were headed for divorce, according to Mary. They have been married less than three years and, thankfully, there were no kids involved.

"Remember last year at Christmas? When I bitched one of my sisters-in-law seemed a little 'too Republican'? She's the one. Darlene. She and Terry were a mismatch from the start. Pretty sure she had her sights set higher than being wife of a high school football coach. Her loss.

"The other two, Joanie and Judy, are great. Bright, too. When their kids get older, they'll go back to work. One taught school, special ed. The other was a trust officer in a bank.

"My brothers may be jocks, but they're not dumb. You guys will get along great. They always want to know what I'm up to in my work. They believe in what I do, working in immigration and all that. They're very protective."

Which brought up something that had been on my mind from the minute Mary first asked me to meet the 'fam.'

"Logistics. What about logistics?" I asked.

"Logistics," she replied. "What do you mean, logistics? Oh, sleeping arrangements?"

Yes, now that you mentioned it.

"Oh, we'll share the same room," Mary answered. "This is new territory for me, too, but we're all adults here.

"My brothers might tease us a bit, but even Dad'll be cool. Don't worry about it. If I recall the layout of the room we'll get, there's only one bed, too."

OK, sounds good.

"There's just one thing, though," she quickly added.

What?

"We'll have to be quieter than usual. The walls are very thin."

Break's over

NO QUESTION, THE week in Steamboat Springs was a perfect escape. Apparently, we weren't too noisy either. No smirks at the breakfast table. We got term papers graded, too.

On our return trip to Indiana we took Interstate 80 across Nebraska and Iowa, successfully outflanking a snowstorm whipping across Kansas.

"How'd I do?" I asked, somewhere between North Platte and Kearney. "Did I get the Jagger Family stamp of approval?"

"Well, aside from looking like a clown on the slopes, you did OK," answered Mary. "I mean, really. The Bunny Trail? I guess we can work on that some more. Maybe get you up to Beginner Level."

Admittedly my skiing did fall short, but I dazzled 'em on a basketball court we discovered in a local recreation center. I whipped all three Jagger brothers in one-on-one contests.

They seemed impressed. "Mary didn't tell us anything about this," said Terry, after his defeat. "I thought you'd be some sort of egghead, teaching in college."

I guessed that was as good as it would get from them.

Our little tournament was followed with additional male bonding: A stop at a sports bar that lasted deep into the night, highlighted—I thought—by tales from my bartending days.

In exchange, I got hilarious tales about pranks they pulled on Mary over the years. It was obvious they loved and respected their sister dearly. Sharing the stories seemed, in a sense, an entry for me into the circle.

Now, as Mary drove the Omaha to Des Moines leg, I finally switched on my cell phone to get caught up on messages. I had left it off for a week, and it was jammed. Aside from spam, many were from students.

Our final exams were administered in late December before the holiday break. There were several complaints about grades, but nothing I couldn't handle.

The real desperation came at the close of the second semester, when graduation hangs in the balance for seniors. Excuses fly like sparks from a bonfire.

There was a text from Jing wishing me a good time on my vacation. She and Kate spent a week in Florida. Her brother, Zhang, who had an American girlfriend from Goshen, visited her family for several days.

By design, none of the Chinese students returned to their homeland despite a nearly three-week long break. We simply did not want to take the chance Chinese officials would clamp down and make them stay home, figuring they'd experienced enough Western culture.

Or, for that matter, would our own INS re-admit them for the second semester? We did not wish to go through that nerve-racker again.

The basketball players stayed in Harrison in the dormitory. Some faculty and staffers invited them to their homes for meals. There were practices and the Louisville tournament. Hopefully, Hu Yang and the gang also got all the time they wanted in the library.

Those not on the team mostly scattered, some making trips in the U.S. to visit homes of new Harrison friends. None that I knew were Christian, so the whole experience of Christmas—or Chanukah, for that matter—undoubtedly would take explaining by hosts.

Nate wanted to organize a New Year's Eve blowout for everyone in the Holy Rollers' farmhouse. Thankfully, he took it OK when I suggested this might not be a good idea. What if there was a DEA raid?

Later in the year, we planned a group visit to the only genuine Chinatown in a thousand miles, Chicago. Two students had relatives living there, including the owner of a popular restaurant. Undoubtedly, we'd get a discounted group meal.

The overall transition thus far appeared smooth. While I was sure there was grumbling among more reactionary townsfolk and alumni, polite society in Harrison had officially embraced the international visitors from what I saw.

On the basketball front, which I also blanked out in Colorado, Harrison had fading results during the holiday tournament. So be it. I was determined to stay aloof.

Judging from the box scores on our college athletic website, the Colonials played sloppily in losing both games to mediocre Wittenberg and Allegheny. Our record still was a respectable 7-2, but we had yet to play a conference team. We were in a downward spiral.

Worse, our next date was in Indianapolis against Indiana State in the state's annual David & Goliath game. This would be played in the Bankers Life Fieldhouse. The game preceded the Indiana Pacers and Cleveland Cavaliers, which meant a huge crowd in addition to a regional TV audience.

This could be embarrassing. Indiana State was hot. The Sycamores came out of the holiday break at 9-0 and, at No, 18, had cracked the major college Associated Press rankings for the first time in over 15 years.

Could it get any worse?

Well, yes. Basketball Hall of Famer Larry Bird, an Indiana State alum, would toss the ball up for the ceremonial tipoff. The Chinese players, students of U.S. basketball, were well aware of his legendary status.

There was no way anyone, in his or her right mind, could have guessed what would emerge from that game.

81

Where's Ollie?

JIMMY WALKED INTO Billy Jack's office. He plopped down luggage not yet unpacked, and asked: "What do we do now?"

A lot happened since Ollie came up missing a week earlier in the Windy City following the victory against Chicago Tech. The assistant coach had remained there, looking in vain for the missing student-athlete.

Most important to Billy Jack, the Buckaroos soldiered their way to three more wins since beating Tech. Two victories were against TriAC weaklings, Baptist College and Oklahoma Lutheran.

On the surface, everything looked good. Perhaps it was a good thing the Buckaroos received no media attention. There were no reporters to note Ollie's absence.

Mesquite was cruising with a 12-0 record, a testament to exquisite scheduling. This elevated it to an unprecedented No. 11 spot in the Associated Press national rankings. At 2-0, they were at the top of the conference standings.

Luke Hodges was pressed into Ollie's starting spot by the coach. Though in need of polishing and stamina, his height proved useful and he began to look like a bona fide basketball player. Never mind the opponents were chopped liver.

Furthermore, help was on the way. While Jimmy was in Chicago scouring neighborhoods for Ollie, Billy Jack worked the phones 24/7 looking for additions to the Mesquite roster. In his world, it never was too late.

This amounted to going over his ever-handy list of ready-made recruits he kept current. Many were enrolled somewhere, but there always was the chance—if he could get to them—to entice someone unhappy to transfer.

What's a little tampering, anyway?

According to NCAA rules for Division III transfers could be eligible to play in the same academic term in which they were admitted. In effect, they could come for just one semester to play and move on. Attending class was optional.

There always was some player out there pissed off about something, looking for a scenery change. His own Buckaroo lineup was Exhibit A.

On the last day to register for the second semester, he did make one addition: Calvin Turner, a pint-sized guard with terrific quickness and ball-handling skills.

Turner came to Mesquite from Central Tennessee University. The transfer was brokered by one of the coach's old pals, a shoe company representative. It was a sight-unseen transaction. Better to not have direct contact or leave a paper trail in these matters, he learned from past experiences.

When Calvin first walked into his office, Billy Jack wondered if maybe he should've been more attentive.

For starters, his newest player looked to be about 5-foot-8 and not 6-foot as advertised.

Next, Calvin quickly informed the coach he no longer was to be called Calvin Turner.

"Changed my name, coach," he said. "I'm converting to Islam. My new name is Mohammad Abdullah. That's what I put down on forms. I'd appreciate it if you'd spread the word. You can call me Mo, if you want."

"Really, Calvin, err, I mean Mohammad," said Billy Jack. "Well, congratulations. Obviously, we'll honor your wishes. How did this happen?"

"Been something I considered a long time, coach. After I got to Central Tennessee and got wheels turning on it, didn't seem to go over well there.

"I mean, you know, I'm from Detroit anyway—and now I'm turning Muslim? Surrounded by hillbillies? Felt I needed a new 'hood, you know?"

"To here?" said the coach, trying not to sound incredulous.

"Yeah, well, figured it'd be a good place to clear my mind before I find something better next season. Not many distractions. Just basket-ball." (Pause.) Oh, and school. Can't forget that."

Billy Jack, to give his newest player a chance to get up to speed, quickly made him the Buckaroos' 6th man. He was quick to go to him on the bench.

The schedule figured to toughen in coming weeks. He needed to create depth if there was to be a long tournament run to the NCAA championship.

"Any way you look at it, we will need Ollie," said the coach. "I don't know what happened in Chicago, but we're not giving up finding him."

Which presented this challenge: The deadline for completing first semester work had passed since his disappearance. Final exams were administered in that stretch. Grades were in the mail.

Of course, this was no problem in Billy Jack's own "Systems" class. With or without him, Ollie's "A" was assured. Already it was entered in the books.

He also was enrolled in an Independent Study course with project deadlines that easily could be stretched. And thus far, in the only legitimate class Ollie took the first semester—Theory of Rodeo 101, the coach covered for him with the professor, who was getting impatient.

"How'd you work that with the teacher?" asked Jimmy.

"Told him there was a death in Ollie's family," the coach said. "That he was needed at home, to help settle complicated family legal matters."

"Man, you can really spread the bullshit," said his assistant.

Actually, Billy Jack was close to convincing the professor that he, his coach, should administer the test since he was in constant contact with Ollie. Never mind he had no clue as to his real whereabouts.

What the hell? This was peanuts. By now, he'd broken a truck load of NCAA regulations and probably was guilty of several felonies with his Jumbo/Jimbo/JJ scam.

What's with a little grade tampering at this point? In for a penny, in for a pound.

Then two weeks after Mesquite's victory in Chicago, there was a soft knock on Billy Jack's closed office door. "Come in," the coach said.

The door opened and Ollie, a bandage on his forehead, entered. "Hey, coach, it's me," he said.

Billy Jack was thrilled to see his star rebounder emerge from the missing, but how to react? Mad? Understanding? Kiss his feet?

Finally, putting personal priorities aside and showing a rare sense of responsibility, the coach proceeded to admonish Ollie for his unexcused absence. Never mind that most coaches would've dismissed him from the program on the spot.

Mostly, Billy Jack stressed to the wayward Buckaroo his lack of loyalty to teammates. The coach figured this angle—laying a guilt trip on his AWOL athlete—would get better results in remaining contests.

An outsider, listening closely, would've noted this: Not once did he ask Ollie why he was absent or express interest in his personal welfare. This was by design, of course. The less a coach knew in this situation, the better.

Truth be told, the Buckaroos fared OK without Maddox, going undefeated in the missed games. The wins were not as impressive, but, with Luke's improved play and the addition of Turner—make that Abdullah, there was plenty of time to recoup.

Furthermore, the issue of Ollie's grades got resolved.

Billy Jack's "A" for him was a given from the get-go, and the coach farmed out the Independent Study project and Rodeo History final to the student manager.

In fact, unknown to Ollie, he made the Mesquite dean's list.

It would not be for a week that Billy Jack, who put Jimmy on the case, would learn exactly what happened: that Ollie, detoured to a party by a cousin following the game against Tech, got caught in a Chicago police sweep.

Though innocent of wrongdoing, the cops arrested him with 14 others for "disturbing the peace" and "resisting arrest." Unable to post bond and scared to call his coach, he sat in the Cook County Jail for a week before relatives sprung him.

Then, it took a Chicago cousin's friend—a pastor for a storefront Baptist Church—to finally talk him into returning to Mesquite.

The bandage on his head?

"You don't want to know, coach." He was right. Billy Jack didn't. No problem.

The punishment? A one-game suspension, but not before Billy Jack checked the schedule to make sure it was against a weak opponent.

If there was concern by the coach, it was this: Ollie's scheduled court appearance would occur while the NCAA finals were played in the Wintrust Arena.

At least both events were in Chicago.

82

Coming out party

LET'S CUT TO the chase. David bumped off Goliath.

Harrison, in perhaps the most stunning upset in Hoosier-land college hoops history, beat Indiana State 81-74 in Indianapolis' Bankers
Life Fieldhouse.

There were 7,000 or so fans in the facility at tipoff for this regionally
televised preliminary game. As word spread of its closeness, basketball
fans planning to attend only the NBA Pacers-Cavaliers main event
hurried to the action. By the final horn, the final count swelled to
18,576 spectators.

That figure, plus a regional TV audience, added up to at least 10
seasons' worth of basketball attendees in Harrison's Miller Fieldhouse.
both men and women's teams.

The Colonials were so impressive Larry Bird came into their locker
room to congratulate Charley as well as each player. He shook everyone's hand, signed autographs, and posed for dozens of pictures.

In Indiana basketball, it does not get bigger.

Mary and I, packed into the Harrison cheering section, yelled ourselves hoarse. Everyone, including the Holy Rollers contingent, rushed
to the floor and swarmed the winning players after their win against the
Sycamores.

The outcome had early-season, national implications. The 24-hour sports news cycle gave it a good run. ESPN led its SportsCenter show with the news.

A photo of huge Nate "The Preacher" Stine bear-hugging and lifting Wang Li and Yang Lu off the floor at the same time, captured by Associated Press, was especially popular with media outlets.

In the Indianapolis newspapers, the outcome was played bigger than the Pacers' expected loss to Cleveland.

Headlines included:

"Sycamores chopped down"
"David topples Goliath"
"Harrison who?"

And, my favorite:

"Chinese take out!"

The outcome appeared to be no fluke. Harrison was running away from an overwhelmed Indiana State in the final minutes. Like many upsets, it was the "how they did it" that was intriguing.

Those scrambled, integrated Colonial lineups? Charley's insistence on refraining from his five best players—the Chinese—playing together at one time?

From the very start of the season, he had a plan in mind for this contest: Two-platoon basketball.

His starting five for this contest were all Chinese, who called themselves the Pandas. Then there was a second five, known as the Eagles.

This backup unit was made up of four returnees from the previous Harrison season plus a sharp-shooting freshman from Kokomo, Jimmy Bradley. The Pandas totaled just under 25 minutes with the Eagles accumulating the balance of the 40-minute game.

The two-platoon system added up to 10 Colonials seeing action in the upset of a nationally-ranked major school, which, by the way, used only eight very-gassed-at-the-end players.

Had Charley hit upon the right formula to keep everyone happy *and* maximize his squad's talent? It sure seemed so. Smart guy.

It was beautiful: Every time Charley ran in one of the platoons, confusion reigned among the Indiana State players. You could see the panic in their eyes. What the hell was this? Who guarded who?

The entire Harrison squad—plus Jing—gathered for a group picture under a basket. The players insisted for her to be in the shot. "She brings us good luck," explained Wang. "In China, she would be our 'cabbage.'"

The Chinese have many symbols for luck and prosperity, including Buddha statues, cats, bamboo pieces, and fish. Somehow, the cabbage seemed to fit. Sort of.

My favorite scene was seeing a tearful Jing and Zhang hugging. It did not seem that long ago I was in their Xiamen home, meeting the parents, dining, and learning valuable lessons about China.

"We are so happy," said Zhang. "My sister is so wonderful to make this happen."

The Pacers and Cavaliers, who watched the final minutes from the wings, high-fived each victorious Colonial as they trooped to the locker room. What a thrill.

The Harrison post-game alumni reception in a downtown hotel was packed. Charley and the players joined the joyous festivities about an hour after the game. The players looked confused, then broke out in big smiles, over the greeting they received after walking into the room.

This was an important breakthrough: If alums had reservations about their alma mater represented by visiting Chinese, the gathering went a long way in breaking barriers.

President Casey was everywhere during the party, working the room as if he were running for political office. As a native of the state, he knew the value of basketball success.

Charley introduced the players, with each Colonial saying a few words. Each player spoke perfect English, which probably was a surprise to the crowd. Jing, unofficial team manager by now, was not needed to translate.

When Charley noted to everyone that Wang Chen, at 6-foot-11 the tallest in the room, was the nephew of former NBA star Yao Ming, there was a gasp.

In his years playing for Houston, Yao had some of his best games against the local Pacers. "That ought to help our image," I whispered to Mary.

On the drive back to Harrison following the upset, I explained Charley's strategy to Mary as he outlined it to me during the festivities.

"A spinoff of the 'Grinnell System,'" I explained. "There's a small college, Grinnell, in Iowa that uses two complete platoons of players and they sub for each other every 2 or 3 minutes.

"Very innovative. They play wide open ball, shooting almost as quick as they cross the center line and full-court press on defense from start to finish. Very high-pressure stuff. See, you can play that way throughout the game since your players are always fresh with the quick subbing.

"It can get sloppy, lots of turnovers and missed shots and that's why coaches don't do it. But if you play that way in every game, you build a comfort zone. You make the other guys try to stay up with you. Eventually most break down and panic. It's just a matter of time.

"Did you see Indiana State players panic when five, totally different players walked on the floor after a timeout? They didn't know who to guard. Their mix-ups cost them at least a half-dozen points. Oh, and a timeout as well when the coach needed to regroup.

"Then they had to go through the same thing again with the next switch. They couldn't get into a rhythm, which is huge in basketball. They'd never seen something like this before.

"See, coaches don't create two platoons because they don't have 10 players they trust. But, in a weird way, the system can make recruiting easier."

"How so?" asked Mary.

Easy, I explained.

With two platoons, you have 10 starting positions instead of the normal five. Since platooning divides the playing time 50-50 and the talent is spread evenly over the two units, you can promise more playing time to more players. That means kids at the lower end get a chance to improve.

But Charley's system is a brilliant spinoff that perfectly fits his personnel, I added.

"How so?" asked Mary, beginning to sound like a broken record.

"He's weighted his platoons. The Pandas, or Chinese, play about 65%. They're clearly more talented and play an up-tempo game that fits their skills. They're taller and get more rebounds, so they shoot a lot. Few teams we'll play can match their skills.

"The Eagles will play about 35% of the time. They're shorter and play more deliberate. They work the ball around a lot more before shooting. They also press, but it is a press that starts at half-court and makes it difficult for the opponent to get into an offensive rhythm. They get trapped.

"Playing the two units also forces the other team into a greater variety of personnel matchups and changing dynamics, which they need to do against us. It drives an opposing coach crazy. Lots of Xs and Os trying to find the right combinations.

"Oh, and the Eagles, who ordinarily would not get as much playing time, now get better as the season progresses. They see more action with platooning. This gives them cohesion, and the team more overall depth. We should be really tough at tournament time, if we qualify."

"Wow!" said Mary. "I got three jock brothers, but never gave much thought to strategies. It's cool that Harrison's doing something innovative like this, too. At the same time, we add something you didn't mention."

What's that?

"Ownership. The rest of the team and our followers aren't just watching a bunch of foreigners win games for us. It's real cutting-edge stuff. Everyone's got an investment. Especially the Eagles."

She was right.

Indianapolis was a perfect venue for Charley to unveil his system, too. We had several thousand followers, many of them alumni, in attendance. Our regular home games do not draw that many fans.

Plus, there were bonuses: The added thousands of spectators on hand at the end and the TV and print publicity.

Almost every daily newspaper in Indiana had sports writers sitting on press row. While they came anticipating the main event, Pacers vs. Cavaliers, they also wrote about the big upset in the preliminary game and got an up-close glimpse—and explanation—of Charley's creativity.

"Only one downer," I added.

"What?"

"Don't forget. We're doing this at the NCAA Division III level—small potatoes. The storyline is Indiana State losing, not us winning. This was one shining moment for us, then I guarantee we slink into small college fog."

I could not have been more wrong.

Back in the groove

IN A REMORSEFUL first game following his suspension, Ollie was a superstar. Mesquite demolished Oklahoma Lutheran in that home contest 101-62.

He scored 31 points and grabbed 19 rebounds. Both totals were season highs for him.

There would be no more discussion regarding his absence. The only lingering problem was that court appearance in March scheduled in the same week as the NCAA tournament.

While there was no guarantee Mesquite even would advance to the Final Four, Billy Jack hated leaving anything to chance. "So, what happens if we do make it that far?" asked Jimmy.

"I'll lean on my father-in-law for some help," he said. "We'll lawyer up and get a continuance, I suppose. Big Hal's as hot for us to win and get out of this dump as we are."

With Ollie back in the lineup, the Buckaroos functioned like a well-oiled machine. There appeared to be no limits. They blitzed through the last few January weeks and early February, turning foes on their schedule into so much road kill.

Turner/Abdullah, with his darting and penetrating, was a welcome addition. If there was a problem, he liked to freelance as a ballhandler and was slow to pick up on Oscar's Spanish-language play calling.

Mesquite led NCAA scoring, averaging 96.7 points per game. Three players were in the Top 5 in individual, offensive categories. A nice balance, too.

J.J. was No. 4 in overall scoring in the nation, hitting 23.2 points per game. Pete "The Gunner" Dantley was No. 3 in three-point shooting accuracy while Ollie was No. 2 in rebounding, averaging 14.1.

Oscar, the Buckaroos' chief playmaker, was close to breaking into the Top 5 for assists. He probably would be, Billy Jack reasoned, if he didn't spend so damn much time on his Team Linguist role.

There was no doubt the point guard was on to something, however. The one-sided outcomes, like some sort of laboratory, provided numerous opportunities to call out plays in Spanish. They almost always clicked with everyone except Mo, the new guy.

While Buckaroo practice sessions used to end with each player shooting 50 free throws, that was now followed by Oscar's vocabulary quizzes. The team was building a nice inventory.

Only once did it backfire. Two starters for Tri-AC opponent Southwestern State were fluent in Spanish and, quickly caught on to what was happening. They translated counter action, but their team still got steamrolled.

Caramba !!

Heading into the final 10 days of the regular season, the Buckaroos were undefeated. The closest thing to a loss was a 12-point victory at Longhorn, where they had to overcome questionable officiating that favored the home team. Two Buckaroos fouled out.

Billy Jack desperately wanted an undefeated regular season. There were 24 contests on the schedule, followed by a conference tournament and the much-anticipated NCAAs.

The winner of the Tri-AC post-season tournament got an automatic berth in the NCAA playoffs. If a different school won the regular-season standings, but flopped in the tourney, typically it got an NCAA berth as well.

Mesquite worked its way at this point up to No. 10 in small-college men's basketball polls. The high rating would almost guarantee a berth in the big show regardless of the conference tournament outcome, but the coach wanted to leave nothing to doubt. He wanted a sweep.

Putting Ollie's disappearance aside, Billy Jack's biggest worry was J.J. and his parole status that did not expire until August. Thus far, no one connected the dots—that J.J., though registered at Mesquite as Jimbo Jackson, was Jumbo and it was a violation for him to be outside Texas borders.

No doubt about it, however. In his second year as head coach at Mesquite, everything was going smooth. Billy Jack considered himself right on schedule to eventually land a big-time job.

There was one growing annoyance, however. The Buckaroo accomplishments generally went unnoticed by the media. The biggest splash remained the previous season's "Earthquake Game."

Their contests rated only 2-3 paragraphs in the Amarillo News, plus the scores were carried by the Associated Press. That was it.

Though he never complained to her about it, Merrilou's cheerleaders seemed to be getting more attention than his team. Werland Fieldhouse was packed for home games, due in no small measure to the troupe's performances.

Their repertoire was greatly expanded. A special halftime show, each with a different theme, dance routines, and special costumes, was incorporated into these appearances.

His wife wrangled an appearance on an Amarillo morning TV show, hosted by a gal pal she befriended in a yoga class at the country club. Their spot went so well it prompted a barrage of invites for appearances at schools, fairs, and clinics.

The TV spot also led to a full-page, color spread in the Amarillo News' Sunday feature section. In addition to the story and pictures, there was a Q & A with Merrilou as well as individual thumbnail sketches of each participant.

The headline read: *"Tiny Mesquite's big show: The cheerleaders."*

Oklahoma Now, a well-respected statewide monthly magazine out of Oklahoma City, had a writer and photographer spend a week with the cheerleaders. A cover story was planned for March, or basketball tournament time.

"You know what would really help don't you, dear?" said Merrilou, on one of their commutes between Amarillo and Beaver Junction.

"No, what?" was his response.

"If the basketball team would go a long way in the tournament," she said. "It would give us a lot more exposure."

"The thought crossed my mind, Honeyboo."

84

"Tippecanoe and China too"

"THE COVER OF Sports Illustrated!! We're on the frickin' cover of Sports Illustrated!! Can you believe it?"

Charley was screaming over the phone. In between shouts and gasps for air, I was able to cobble everything together.

An SI writer, Sally Garcia, was in the Bankers Life Fieldhouse the night we upset Indiana State. Her assignment was to cover the showdown between the NBA Pacers and Cavaliers, but she became intrigued by our upset and how it was achieved.

The SI writer had downplayed when—and if—her story would appear in the magazine. She pledged her campus sources to silence. "Sometimes these things get spiked," she told Charley. "I don't want to get anyone's hope up."

I was oblivious and that was good. As far as I could see, the basketball program did not need my assistance. Now I was concentrating on teaching. Finally.

Or so I thought.

My second call that morning came from President Casey, who wanted to assemble his own "ad hoc China team," nicknamed by him the "China Cabinet," in the wake of this new media development.

The SI spread was a gift from heaven, but how should we handle the expected surge in interest now that Harrison's story was "national"? How could the college leverage the publicity?

The president had advance copies of the Sports Illustrated magazine for each of us when our "cabinet" convened that afternoon. It was beautiful. Other schools would kill to be in our position, even the big universities. Nothing in school history could compare to this, he said.

The cover showed Harrison players standing on the fieldhouse floor celebrating the Indiana State win. They were gathered around a smiling Wang Chen, who, with a fist raised high in triumph, towered above his teammates.

The headline read: "*Tippecanoe and China too.*" For the American history impaired, this was a reference to the college's namesake, President William H. Harrison.

His campaign battle cry for election to the White House in 1840 was "Tippecanoe and Tyler too." The battle of Tippecanoe was where he made his bones as a military man before entering politics. John Tyler was his running mate.

The inside photos looked as if President Casey ordered them. They focused on our international players, of course, and showed them mixing in a variety of school and community activities, in addition to practicing basketball.

The kill shot? Undoubtedly it was the picture taken one morning when a staffer was shown admitting the Chinese into the library at 6 a.m., two hours before it officially opened.

Athletes getting an early start on their studies? No way. Unheard of. "No one would believe this if I told them," said President Casey. "Now I have proof!"

Sally Garcia's story was as friendly as the photos.

In addition to delving into Charley's innovative two-platoon system, she talked with both the Panda and Eagle platoons, professors impressed with the visiting players' classroom work, regular students including Kate McDonald, and, of course, Casey.

Jing, acknowledged as a team mascot of sorts, worked her way into the story. She apologized to me in our next class for not telling me. "I was sworn to secrecy," she said. "It was very difficult to keep quiet. You know me, Professor Doyle."

With Sports Illustrated not scheduled to hit newsstands for a day, the purpose of this meeting was to organize a flow chart for response to the expected landslide of interest and requests. "We need to be as professional as we can," said the president.

The college's small, public relations staff, good only for producing cliché-riddled press releases rarely used beyond the local newspaper, was way out of its element.

Quickly, our meeting came to the conclusion: Harrison needed outside help. Now. From a consultant or PR firm. Some sort of short-term arrangement to deal with outsiders and their needs, someone who knew the difference between the Boonville Gazette and the Boston Globe.

"The problem, as always, people, is money," said President Casey. "This is something we never dreamed of as a budget item. My discretionary funds are drying up fast."

It was trustee Gil Munson who came up with a splendid solution: Let's find a Harrison alum, retired or still active, who was in the marketing business.

Perhaps we could work out some sort of in-kind giving pact, or, better yet, this person would work pro bono out of loyalty to their alma mater.

Within two days we had our person: Jeanne Martin, a 1987 grad with a perfect background. She ran her own, small communications firm in Indianapolis after a decade or so working in PR for the Indianapolis Colts football team.

In short, she knew how to work with the media, national and local. She knew what reporters needed, and how to be helpful. Better yet, she, with her sports background, was anxious to help. In fact, she was at the Indiana State upset and joined post-game festivities.

My contribution: We drafted two capable upper-class students to provide internal support for Jeanne. Their tasks included taking telephone calls, delivering messages, coordinating interviews and campus tours, and creating our own social media imprints.

We called them interns, which figured to look great on their resumes. They didn't get paid, but they were thrilled to be part of the campus buzz. Jing, our good luck "cabbage," helped them communicate with the Chinese players.

Our plan was good. The telephone never stopped ringing.

The Harrison games suddenly became sellouts, home and road, following the upset. Everyone wanted to see the giant-killing school that played two-platoon basketball with an international touch.

It was a publicity bonanza for the college, sure to bode well for future admissions and donations. Our development department put in overtime.

On the print side, the New York Times, Louisville Courier-Journal, Indianapolis Star, Wall Street Journal, USA Today and Basketball Weekly were among notable publications doing original stories on Charley and the team.

An Associated Press wire piece was carried by dozens of smaller, lesser-known publications as far away as San Juan and Honolulu. We got requests for press credentials for home basketball games. No one in Colonial athletics could recall that happening for any of our sports.

Broadcast? An ESPN-TV feature was a given and we got it. The TV stations in the region, including those in Louisville and Indianapolis, did features. We were the feel-good wrap-up story one weeknight on CBS-TV's network newscast. "60 Minutes" expressed interest.

Another first for Harrison: No one could recall TV trucks, with large satellite dishes on the roofs, vying for parking spaces in the Miller Fieldhouse lot.

But one media spread left my teaching colleagues absolutely peeing in their pants.

This was a feature piece by the Chronicle of Higher Education, academia's Holy Grail. There are professors who've built entire careers just getting a letter-to-the-editor printed in the Chronicle, let alone be identified as a source for a story.

The article focused on the high degree of studiousness demonstrated by our Chinese student-athletes. President Casey, our registrar, and the school librarian were interviewed, in addition to Charley and students

Only one faculty member was quoted. That would be me, who had been teaching full-time all of three semesters. I am sure this thoroughly annoyed Dean Brunk and the tenured old guard, who'd give a month's pay to be regarded as an expert Chronicle source on anything.

Mary did her best to deflate my ego, but it was an impossible task. On the other hand, I could tell she was pleased—and excited—as all of us over how well this barrier-breaking cultural adventure developed. Maybe more so, given her work in Mexico.

Everyone loves a winner and it didn't hurt that the Colonials kept doing exactly that. They jumped into Little-MAC Conference play following the upset and rattled off six straight victories to go 13-2.

The school made its first-ever appearance in the top 20 college rankings at No. 16, a very lofty debut. This undoubtedly was helped by our national media splash.

The situation had its detractors, of course. There was a fair amount of "America first" criticism, people upset we had foreigners on the floor. I saw the word "Chink" on more than a few letters and e-mails received by the school.

One of my favorite letters-to-the-editor comments in the Indianapolis Star: "It's bad enough the basketballs we use in the games are made in China. Now, Chinese athletes are using them."

We kept the players sheltered from the glare. We brought in a computer wizard to teach them social media safeguards for their phones and laptops.

And, of course, the Holy Rollers never were far away.

"I'm spending so much time in the neighborhood maybe I ought to enroll in some classes," Nate said to me one day, when I bumped into him in the fieldhouse.

"I never did get a degree. Maybe I could finish up here. Take one of your classes, Pilgrim. What do you think?"

One totally unexpected wrinkle: A call from the Chinatown Chamber of Commerce in Chicago, which wanted to organize a charter-bus excursion to one of our remaining home contests. It would be a 500-mile round trip.

Wow. It was not that long ago we thought a post-season trip to Chicago's Chinatown would be a nice treat for the entire squad.

Now, Chinatown was coming to us.

Opportunity knocks

BILLY JACK STALKED into Jimmy's office. He plopped the magazine down on his assistant's desk.

"Damnit, you see this Sports Illustrated?" he asked. "The cover, for God's sake. They got a cover story."

Jimmy picked up the magazine. Gazed at the cover, then thumbed to the inside and quickly browsed the spread devoted to Harrison College's basketball program.

"Yeah, so?"

Billy Jack, staring out the office and its view of a treeless prairie, was steamed. "We're kicking ass, doing stuff that's never been done, and nobody knows. We don't get squat from the news media."

"Yeah, so?"

"Well, who are these guys? Hamilton, Harrison or whatever. Never heard of it. They're just a small school like us. A bunch of Chinks fall in their lap, and everyone gets excited. Pisses me off, that's all."

Billy Jack was on a roll.

"We're making history down here, Jimmy. We're undefeated, and I got a Muslim playing alongside an Iraqi military vet, Vic. I got a guard teaching Spanish to his teammates, and we got top 5 guys in a bunch of national categories."

"Yeah, well, don't forget, Coach, you got J.J. You want people to know his story?"

This, of course, got Billy Jack's attention. It was late in the season, playoffs were just around the corner, and, truth be told, the coach was exhausted.

Figuring out strategical Xs and Os, plus the grinding schedule with road games that required long-distance bus travel, were getting to him. He got little administrative help, too.

Toss in commutes from Amarillo to his Beaver Junction office, keeping Merrilou happy, and the constant extinguishing of fires like Ollie's in Chicago, would have sent lesser coaches screaming into the desert sunset.

And, in a most recent development, the stakes got raised for Billy Jack.

This occurred two days earlier with a telephone call. His name was Burt Galloway. He was calling to get a feel for any interest Billy Jack might have in a possible head coaching job at Waco State University in Texas.

Not an official call, however. Strictly speaking, Galloway was not on the Waco payroll. Better yet, it was the other way around. You could say the school was on his payroll, considering the gobs of money he'd donated over the years to his alma mater.

Billy Jack did some quick thinking. He vaguely recalled Waco State, an underachieving NCAA Division II school populated mostly by commuter students. In Division II, you could give real basketball scholarships. No more rodeo "ghost" scholarships.

Undoubtedly, this kind of move would make Merrilou happier. She'd be closer to her beloved Houston. On the other hand, the program always would be overshadowed by Baylor University also in Waco.

But Billy Jack became very alert as the conversation progressed.

In what would be an announcement at the end of the current season, the school planned to make the plunge into Division I. Big time. Galloway, Waco's biggest and richest (software speculation) booster, and with the university president in his hip pocket, would provide the necessary backing.

Bingo! Scholarships, large arenas, radio show, shoe deal, big staff, plush hotels, national scouting, and maybe a private jet. No more bus rides from Beaver Junction to Claremore.

"We'll need energy right from the start, if this thing's going to work," Galloway said. "That means, ahem, ahem, a young and ambitious coach. That's not how you'd describe the current guy. He's personable, but he's a dead man walking as far as I'm concerned."

Burt went on to indicate Billy Jack was exactly the kind of person Waco State would want for the job. While he was not an official representative of the university, he definitely could make things happen.

And exactly how did he learn of what Billy Jack was accomplishing at Mesquite, not exactly center stage in college athletics?

Turns out Galloway lived in Houston, where he was a golfing buddy of Big Hal.

For Billy Jack, this would be a giant move down the yellow brick road even if it meant getting deeper into his father-in-law's debt. Get this program off the ground, then scoot to an established "mid-major" like New Mexico State or Bradley before landing in the big time.

He was right on schedule. An NCAA championship this season would secure the next step. A little publicity would help, too.

86

Showdown

WHITEY LIT UP like a lightbulb when I walked into his saloon.

"Hello, stranger. 'Bout time you dropped by. Thought I'd have to take your dollar bill down from the ceiling. Where's your better half?"

It had been awhile, but it was a slow week. My students were busy on special projects, Mary was attending a conference in Evansville, and there was no basketball game. Not even a faculty meeting to attend. That alone called for a celebration.

Time to take a deep breath and check the "town & gown" pulse, get the real grassroots' skinny. No better place than Whitey's.

"Yeah, you guys are on a real roll," he said, in between serving drinks. "Exciting stuff. I made it to a few home games. People are buzzing. No question."

"So," I asked, "do you think there's resentment? You know. A bunch of foreigners representing Harrison?"

"Naaah. Not now. There might've been some at the start, when things seemed to be sliding downhill. Then, I heard grumbling. But that two-platoon stuff has everyone talking. No one here's seen anything like that. I sure the hell haven't. Fun to watch."

"Purely Charley's idea," my response. "I'm just a Harrison basketball spectator these days."

"Yeah, right, like you had nothing to do with getting the Chinese. Well, it should be clear sailing to the NCAAs the way everyone sees it. Just one big hurdle left, right?"

Whoa. "Hurdle?"

"Well, don't we have Delaware College left to play? The Carson kid's new team?"

Rarely did I try to look past the next game, but Whitey was correct. Though both schools were in the Middle American Conference, or "Little MAC," we were in the league's South Division, Delaware was in the North.

The divisions were big enough to preclude playing everyone in the regular season. This year it was our schools' turn to not play a cross-over contest with each other.

The champs of the respective divisions—and we both were headed in that direction—always met for a post-regular season playoff. The prize? The winner got the league's automatic NCAA bid.

Sometimes, not always, the loser also got an at-large berth into the NCAA tournament. I couldn't see how we'd miss either way, not with everyone following us.

Deny Harrison—a media magnet with its "system"—an at-large berth if we lost to Delaware? The NCAA couldn't be that stupid, could it?

Well, as it developed, we did meet after tying down our respective Little MAC division titles in the final games. We swept to finish a perfect 14-0 in league play, 23-2 in all games. The Indians went 14-0, 24-1.

Delaware, which still called itself the Indians—one of the few schools in America to do this—always had a strong program. The Colonials hadn't had a winning season in nine years.

Despite not having a better overall record, Harrison climbed all the way to No. 5 in the national poll and the Indians were No. 11. This only figured to give our opponent added incentive.

Delaware had a strong team, but the surprise addition of Carson made them better. And factor this in: Brad Carson Sr., the hothead father who made life miserable for Charley, shadowed the Colonials almost the entire season to scout us. He knew more about our players than Charley. Or, at least I'm sure he thought he did.

The showdown was on a very hostile Delaware College floor, due to its overall better record. This was seemingly offset by referees imported from the Big Ten.

Our long drive to the Ohio school resembled a military caravan, with Nate's Holy Rollers in full colors on their choppers accompanying the 25 or so other vehicles with the bus. Mary and I, plus another faculty couple, were somewhere in the middle.

Our armada turned a few heads when we passed through towns.

During the game, the Rollers took customary seats directly behind our bench. The better to know Harrison had strong—emphasis, *strong*—backing. Mary and I scrunched into space in the middle of a Colonial crowd in which townsfolk and alums outnumbered students.

From my vantage point, I could see Brad Carson—the father—sitting directly behind the Indians' bench only a whisper away from the coach. He was armed with a clipboard and laptop, obviously jammed with notes and counter strategies gleaned from tailing the Colonials.

If you didn't know better, he could be mistaken for an assistant coach. It had to be all he could do to not join the huddles during timeouts.

After transferring, his son—Brad Jr.—quickly became a featured player in Delaware's program, leading the team in scoring. A date with his old school was uppermost on his mind from the first Indians' practice.

Harrison's odyssey captivated Indiana (the Indianapolis newspapers were staffing this playoff—a first), but the Carsons were primed. They were not intimidated.

Cocky might be an apt description, but not at the end of this game.

In fact, it took only a few minutes for the matchup to be thrown into chaos for Delaware. Charley unveiled a brilliant, new strategy.

Oh, he played two platoons—the better to wear down the opponent. But for the first time, he scrambled their makeup. Chinese and Americans teamed together. Two Pandas traded places with Eagles on each unit.

This entirely changed the dynamics. It was as if two, new teams had come to play Delaware. And Charley tricked it up even more: The separate platoons took shorter, but equal, shifts putting the Indians even more on their heels.

In effect, their playbook—Brad Carson Sr.'s to be precise—was worthless. Our leading scorer with 19 points was Jimmy Bradley, the freshman hot shot from Kokomo.

In your face, Delaware. Final score: Colonials 85, Indians 68.

NCAAs, here we come.

Growing audience

JEANNE MARTIN? THE Harrison alum who agreed to navigate our Harrison basketball ship through media waters?

Jeanne maintained—jokingly, I think—that she was having a blast throughout the adventure. But that was before the latest request.

"Flip, I think you better get over to my office as soon as you can," said President Casey. "I've got Jeanne sitting here now. You need to be in on this."

I beat my, by now, well-worn path to the administration building. I seemed to be spending more time in the president's office than classrooms. No matter, but this was getting almost funny.

"Tell him, Jeanne," he said, almost the instant I entered.

"You know a Hu Jun and a Maggie Wei, right?" she started. "They said you'd remember. I got a call from their people yesterday, or today, or whatever time it was in China when I got it. Turns out they're following our basketball; they're interested in turning it into a project."

Hu and Maggie? Part of that Chinese film delegation back in Iowa City? The group I sipped beers with in the Airport and reminisced about teaching in Xiamen? And did a story on them in USA Today that went global? A lifetime ago?

Well, yes.

"They want us, Harrison College, to be part of a documentary they're working on," she said.

"No shit. I mean, no kidding."

Jeanne did not have entire details, but the documentary would be part of Hu's ongoing quest to integrate Western culture into the Chinese filmgoer experience. This sounded very familiar to me.

The total "Americana" project would consist of five, 30-minute segments. One would be devoted to us and highlight the Chinese students' experience. The other four would cover various, unrelated topics. They'd be marketed and viewed separately, or sometimes in one package.

"Maggie said they like our story because it touches many bases—small town America, education, sports, etc.," added Jeanne. "Viewers in China will see the U.S. in a way that's never shown. No science fiction or gore. Real life. Also, it'll give them some new 'Little Fresh Meat,' whatever that means."

I laughed, then explained the "Meat" concept. It was nothing erotic, I assured, and this drew collective relief. It simply meant, fresh new—and young—faces shown on a screen. It also meant Jing and the gang might be on the verge of becoming big stars in their homeland.

Jeanne continued, ""Well, Maggie did mention Hu liked a narrative through the eyes of millennials and younger ages, a huge attraction for China's moviegoing public. The documentary would be shown on mainstream TV and over five thousand big screen theatres."

We sat there for a minute without saying anything, smiling and adding up in our minds what it could mean for this remote little college in southern Indiana burg named for a forgotten U.S. president.

The possibilities were mind-boggling for Harrison. The brains in the room were connecting dots so fast you could almost hear them humming. Or was that noise the sound of cash registers at work?

For President Casey: A larger, more selective enrollment, new buildings, more faculty, new departments, perhaps an entire China Studies major, exchange programs, successful capital campaigns, endowment growth, happy new alums with well-paying jobs, and on and on.

For Jeanne, someone I did not know that well, it probably went this way: Wow! This could be a gold mine for my communications company, offering services to Chinese universities. I could open more offices.

Me? Maybe I should ask for tenure. Or a raise, at least.

Finally, I broke the silence.

In what may have been the understatement of our meeting, I said: "No doubt. This could be huge. What do we tell them?"

"We've already told them yes," said Jeanne. "They're on their way with a crew and should arrive tomorrow."

"Well, let's just hope we win a few games, give them lots of footage."

88

Cheering them on

THE MESQUITE "TOURNAMENT bid" celebration was historic. No one could recall such an event held on the campus, not even for the many Buckaroo rodeo titles.

Werland Fieldhouse was packed. Was it the free food? Free tee-shirts?

Billy Jack didn't care. This was the way the big boys did it in major college basketball, and that's why he insisted on an event to hype getting the inevitable NCAA playoff invitation that would follow the conference title.

What the hell. It was expensive, but Big Hal, who was on hand, helped cover costs including a film crew he flew in from Houston. Balloons, streamers, pennants for every attendee, commemorative baseball caps, the whole works.

He arranged for chartered buses to transport every school kid within a 50-mile radius. Of course, given that this was remote Oklahoma panhandle country, that did not necessarily add up to many more butts in the seats.

More important, Hal brought his buddy Burt Galloway, the Waco State booster. This gave him a chance to get a close-up look at his No.1 candidate to lead the school's dream to go big-time.

The event's scheduled highlight: The NCAA announcement of the entire 64-team field, and their pathway to the championship, piped onto a big screen. It was shown on a closed-circuit stream arranged specially for the school, another added expense.

There was no secret that Mesquite would get a berth, of course.

The Buckaroos, regaining momentum with the return of Ollie and the addition of Mohammad, blitzed their way past every opponent in the schedule's final weeks.

Their mark was a perfect 26-0, with a 98.2 scoring average per game. Nine times they surpassed 100 points, an NCAA record. Three players finished top 5 in separate offensive categories.

The team's final margin of victory—23.6 points per win—also was an NCAA record. To get this mark, the Buckaroos left in their wake plenty of pissed off coaches who felt scores got run up against them. Tough. This was business.

With its dazzling stretch run, Mesquite leapfrogged its way to No. 2 in the rankings.

No. 1 was Milton College, an East Coast school that won the previous year's NCAA title and held the top rating throughout the season. The Poets, a perennial contender, also finished 26-0.

Billy Jack, who never quite got over the publicity that school in Indiana (Harrison) received, smirked a bit when his Buckaroos jumped over it in the next-to-last poll. The Colonials, considered a bit of fluke by some purists, ranked No. 6.

Mesquite's very high seeding put it on a possible collision course with Milton in the championship contest in Chicago's Wintrust Arena. The Buckaroos would start their quest in a regional tournament in the United Super Markets Arena in Lubbock, Texas.

Billy Jack saw this as a good omen, considering J.J. would not be in violation of the terms of his parole playing in Texas. Never mind that he was competing under a false identity.

After winning the regional to be among 16 surviving teams—a forgone conclusion in the coach's mind—the Buckaroos would see its next two games played in Dodge City, Kan.

The announcement was met with a rousing rendition by the pep band of the school song, which borrowed heavily from the melody of "On Wisconsin." The cheerleaders, fast becoming local legends with their TV and print exposure, unveiled several new routines.

Billy Jack's pep talk and introduction of players were to follow, but then a strange thing happened: This part of the program—supposedly the highlight—got delayed 15 minutes.

Merrilou's debut routines for the occasion were so compelling— splits, somersaults, handsprings (forward & backward), a four-layered pyramid with a "flyer"—the cheerleaders got called for three encores.

It probably helped that the coeds' extremely skimpier, new cheer uniforms also unveiled were, to be honest, not far from being illegal in this Bible Belt region.

"Damn," Galloway whispered to Big Hal. "Maybe your Merrilou can get them to come to Waco and cheer for us, too."

The happy couple's post-rally car ride back to Amarillo?

Merrilou was on a high, ecstatic over the reception for her cheerleaders.

"Incredible, Billy!! Really incredible. Never saw a crowd respond like that. Just for us, too. We could've had more encores. Wait'll we get home. I can't wait to call my friends. So glad it's on film. Daddy was a prince to bring in that crew."

Yeah, a prince, thought Billy Jack. His forced smile took effort. Sure, he was pleased Merrilou had found "a calling" in HIS big adventure.

But no question he was increasingly annoyed. Bad enough that school in Indiana, Hamilton or whatever, got so much publicity with its Chinks.

But to get overshadowed in his own backyard? By his wife's cheerleaders?

That's probably why he barely could look happy with his wife's next nugget.

"Daddy was so excited today he's entering us in the national collegiate cheering competition. This is big, Billy. We just made the deadline."

CHAPTER

89

Mapping it out

ANOTHER DAY, ANOTHER trip to meet with President Casey. Well, this meeting definitely *was* different.

On little notice, a small group got invited to the president's manse for dinner. Hu Jun and Maggie Wei were guests of honor. They brought their chief cinematographer, Wang Wei, head writer, Li Na, and film editor, Ding Wing.

These five from China, plus another dozen or so in the crew who stayed in their motel rooms to catch up on sleep, arrived the night before at O'Hare in Chicago. They quickly loaded rental vans and, presumably with MapQuest, found the way to Harrison in downstate Indiana.

They were ready to go to work.

On our "side" were President Casey, Jeanne Martin, Gil Munson representing trustees, me, Mary (my suggestion) and Dean Brunk, an invitation I figured to be "good politics" on the president's part.

Also in our Harrison group: Lee Yang, our lone Chinese-American faculty member who was born in Milwaukee and, as far as I knew, had never set foot in China. He taught biology and spoke no Chinese whatsoever.

The gathering started as a bit of a reunion. Hu and Maggie were happy to see me, recalling our sessions at the Airport in Iowa City. They seemed especially enthused over the story I wrote about them that went viral.

Apparently, the article opened more doors for them, in the U.S. as well as China. I, of course, acted humble. Inwardly, I was thrilled. President Casey, Dean Brunk and others in our group had to be impressed.

The ubiquitous Jing, an excellent translator—both linguistically and culturally—was there as well. She was in the U.S. less than a year, but not surprisingly proved to be a quick learner. Already she knew the difference between a Grammy and an Emmy.

I gave Jing strict orders: Do not ask for Hu Jun's autograph despite the fact he is, according to her, the "Steven Spielberg" of Chinese films. This was to be kept strictly professional.

Left out: Charley Cunningham, our basketball coach, at the request of our visitors. They wanted as little contact as possible at the entry point with principles likely to appear in the film, the better to keep things spontaneous and honest.

Essentially, we gave the visitors a basketball road map—from A to Z—for the Harrison team. Additionally, we tossed in geography, demographics, U.S. educational system, and other relevant issues. Charley's unique, two-platoon attack raised eyebrows.

They took copious notes, frequently interrupting to ask questions. When our answers prompted excited exchanges among them in Mandarin, or whatever dialect, our side smiled, nodded, and paid attention as if we understood every word.

Harrison was assigned to the Midwest Region. Our pathway figured to give them a real slice of Americana. College basketball is not always the glamorous world the public is led to believe.

Our visitors seemed a bit surprised over our small-college status. They assumed we competed alongside schools such as Duke, North Carolina, Kentucky, and UCLA. There are no Madison Square Gardens in our world.

The first stop for us was a regional tournament in Paducah, Ky., an Ohio River community not far downstream from our college. We would be playing in the National Quilt Show & Expo Convention Center, a 7,500-seat facility.

The other schools assigned to this site with us were: Transylvania University (Ky.), Rose-Hulman Institute of Technology (Ind.) and Eureka College (Ill.), our opening foe.

Four schools with absolutely nothing else in common but basketball teams. Perfect.

"I am liking this more and more," Hu said. "My feeling is that we will be seeing—what is it Americans say?—grassroots. There will be no New York City or Los Angeles. This is very good, very fresh for Chinese audiences."

Well, yes. Grassroots was one way to describe our world. If he wanted it, we could provide it.

If we won the Regional to join the surviving Sweet 16 teams, a first for Harrison, the Sectional tourney site would be in Fargo, N.D., in that city's North Dakota Beef Processors Arena, an 8,000-seat venue.

From there, of course, it was the Final Four in Chicago's Wintrust Arena.

Quilt Show Hall, Beef Processors Arena, Wintrust Arena? The visitors seemed fascinated by the facilities' names. The public stadiums in China tended to have names such as The People's Industrial Labor Gymnasium and Universal Centre for Sport & Fitness.

Hu's plan was two-pronged. He would follow the Chinese players and capture the experience through their eyes. In the end, he would use only two of those filmed that he deemed most colorful.

At the same time, he would assign remaining crews to follow other students in and out of classrooms. There also would be interviews with faculty and townspeople, picked at random.

In effect, the visitors got *carte blanche*. They were only vaguely sure at this point about a final storyline. That would emerge in China, when they returned and looked at raw takes. They were especially impressed to have a free hand.

"We will see how things develop over time," Hu said. "This is—how do you say in America?—an organic production. It is best. It is how I can make things real. This is not to be fiction."

From Paducah to Chicago, with a stop in Fargo.

"I would very much like to get to Chicago," Hu added. "I understand there is a good Chinatown there with many fine restaurants. I would like to see this very much."

The key to everything, we agreed, was for the Colonials to win games and keep advancing. This was the sure way to give our newly-acquired entourage lots of footage.

We assured our visitors this would be no problem. What could go wrong?

VI

Fast start

THAT FIRST WEEK of NCAA tournaments was a blur for Mesquite, which rolled into the competition with its perfect season. Billy Jack kept his team under tight wraps in Lubbock, when the Buckaroos assembled two nights before their opener.

His team was pitted against Alamo College. The other two schools in the Regional Field playing each other were Sam Houston State and Stephen F. Austin State, bitter in-state rivals who'd split their home-and-home series during the regular season.

"You've got schools named for two Texas legends and another for The Alamo in the field," wrote local sports columnist Slim Jenkins. "This isn't a basketball tournament. It's a lesson in Texas history. Good luck to the outsiders from Oklahoma."

All humor was lost on the Mesquite contingent, of course. Yes, it had the best regular season in school history under its belt, but now it was time to get to work.

Just as Billy Jack hoped to morph an NCAA title into a better job, this concept was not lost on his players: A championship would make them more attractive as transfers to better programs. They'd get real scholarships for basketball, not rodeo. It was a ticket out of Beaver Junction.

Billy Jack allowed one "educational" outing in Lubbock: A visit to a museum dedicated to native son Buddy Holly. His players had zero knowledge of the rock and roll legend, but they were fascinated to learn he died in an airplane crash at age 22. Five Buckaroo squad members were older.

Billy Jack and Jimmy took shifts camping out nights in the team's Fairfield Inn lobby. There would be no reccurrences of Ollie's misadventures in Chicago, which resulted in a court appearance hanging over the team.

Just to be on the safe side, Merrilou's cheerleaders were booked in the DoubleTree on Lubbock's opposite side. The coach couldn't help notice several Buckaroos had become more than a little friendly with her squad members.

Mesquite made short work of Alamo College in its opener, 102-63. The Buckaroos, after all, were seeded No. 2 in the 64-team field. The second game, a 97-80 win against Sam Houston State, was slightly more competitive. Early mismatches were common, considering ratings were unscientific.

Mercifully, Billy Jack pulled his starters with nearly 10 minutes to play against Alamo. By then Oscar worked on, and pretty much perfected, a new Spanish language play. It was *"prensa de media cancha,"* a signal to apply a variation on a half-court press.

Admittedly it looked cruel to be pressing while holding a 30-point lead. On the other hand, reasoned Billy Jack, it was a bit surprising a Texas school named for The Alamo had no one who could speak, or understand, Spanish.

Mohammed, first off the bench in the team's scheme, ran the show the last 10 minutes. His innocent suggestion several weeks earlier that Islamic slogans also be used to signal plays got quickly dismissed.

Whaaa? One of my players calling out plays to attack an opponent using Muslim chants? Just what we needed, the coach thought to himself, before replying.

"Err, two foreign languages might be a bit much for the boys," said Billy Jack, as soon as color returned to his face. "Some have enough trouble with one. It's a little late in the season to start. Maybe next year."

91

Eureka !!

"A journey of a thousand miles must begin with a single step."
—Ancient Chinese proverb

THE FIRST STOP on the Harrison College basketball trail, Paducah, Ky., was only 140 miles or so downstream on the Ohio River. The National Quilt Show & Expo Convention Center, where games were played, was in the center of town—and, a museum alongside, the community's economic heartbeat.

Turns out there are something like 21 million quilters in the U.S., making it a billion-dollar industry. Every year the annual Quilt Week convention and competition in Paducah draws thousands of participants from 50 or so nations around the globe. Who knew?

"You've got to get out more, Flip," Mary finally responded, as I continued to rattle off more amazing—to me—factoids from brochures. "Quilting's a big deal. Just doesn't get mainstream publicity."

To get to Paducah, our Harrison motorized caravan required a more circuitous route of back roads through small towns. The trip took nearly four hours. Too bad we couldn't float there on the river.

In the history of vehicular travel, it's quite possible our entourage turned more heads and got more stares per capita than any fan-generated caravan in motorized history. And why not?

The armada stretched nearly a mile. Near the front, there were two huge, Greyhound-style chartered buses carrying the official party of players, coaches, staff, equipment and luggage.

Behind this were two panel trucks, with satellite dishes atop, that were rented by the Chinese film crew. Then, as arranged by Jeanne Martin, there were two media cars carrying additional production people, sportswriters and a Sports Illustrated stringer writing a follow to the spread the publication gave us.

There also were dozens and dozens of automobiles with fans, including three vehicles from Indianapolis TV stations. Some local businesses, including Whitey, offered rides in station wagons, SUVs, and RVs adorned with signs.

Immediately in front of the big buses were two Harrison County sheriff's department cars with red lights flashing. There was one Indiana Highway Patrol car in the mix, too.

Oh, and let us not forget: Nate and his Holy Rollers. About 20 choppers with riders in full colors—leather jackets, chaps, boots, red bandanas, no helmets—fronted the caravan. Another 20 or so brought up the rear.

Hey, everybody loves a parade.

When the buses pulled up to the official hotel near the expo hall, another surprising sight unfolded. Waiting for the Harrison contingent were several hundred Chinese-Americans from Chicago, waving pennants and banners.

That city's Chinatown Chamber of Commerce chartered three buses of supporters, who'd been following Harrison—in the media—ever since the SI article. They were led by a chatty fellow named Willy Wong.

Jing, assuming her role as team social director, was everywhere meeting the new-found Colonial supporters and making introductions. She may have been part of the "lost girl" generation in China, but in America she found more friends than a Chicago pol seeking re-election.

Our players, both the Pandas and Eagles, were thrilled, quickly mixing with their new-found followers. In what had to be a first, they got asked for autographs.

Wong, the Chamber of Commerce's executive director, told us later there was no problem organizing the outing. This guy knew how to get things done.

"As soon as I saw there was a riverboat casino in Paducah, it was easy sell," he confided. "I probably fill another bus or two. My people love casinos."

Irrepressible Willy added, "We cannot wait for you to get to Chicago to play for the championship. Chinatown is not far from the arena where you will be playing. This will be bigger than our Chinese New Year celebration."

Little Eureka College had something to say about that, however.

With a little under 90 seconds remaining in our first-round game with the Dutch Boys, Harrison trailed by eight points. We were on the verge of elimination in the opener!

Chicago? Dream on. We looked to be headed back to our own campus. Were we tired from all the excitement? Had we been too confident? Did we read too many press clippings?

It did occur to many in the convention center that Eureka, a downstate Illinois college, was playing over its head. Speaking of which, the tallest starter was a mere 6-foot-4.

The Dutch Boys got into the tournament through the backdoor, earning a spot by catching fire and winning its conference tournament—despite nine regular season losses, most of any school in the 64-team tournament field.

This was embarrassing.

Eureka, at a little less than 800 students, also was one of the smallest schools in the field. This was its first-ever appearance in the tourney. It's biggest claim to sports fame? Future U.S. President Ronald Reagan was a 1932 graduate and played football there.

The Dutch Boys couldn't miss a shot and it did not matter which of our platoons was on the floor. They continued to run the shot clock down on every possession, then fired in 3-pointers.

Our huge height advantage meant nothing. There were no rebounds. They connected on their shots at an unheard of 80% rate.

In the end, we needed a miracle and got it. Trailing 78-70 with 1:29 remaining, Wang Chen was moved to the top of the free throw circle on defense in hopes his 6-foot-11 frame—and immense wingspan—could disrupt Eureka's backcourt passing.

It did. His first blocked pass led to a quick fast break and Harrison bucket by Hu Yang to make the score 78-72. Then, standing in front of the Eureka in-bounds passer with arms outstretched, another block by Chen led to another quick follow-up basket to make it 78-74 with 1:12 remaining.

Eureka, which had no timeouts remaining to regroup, came apart.

Twice more the big guy blocked inbound passes. The first led to another basket, making 78-76, but on the second steal the ball got flipped to our perimeter.

There, Jimmy Bradley, playing with the Panda unit because of Wang Li's foul trouble, drilled a three-pointer to make 79-78 in our favor. There was 1 second remaining. Game, set, and match.

"I was not worried," said Chen, in all seriousness following the game. "We had our cabbage (Jing) with us. We could not lose."

Our second game two nights later, a 90-76 win against Transylvania, a Kentucky school, thankfully was less suspenseful. The Colonials led from the start, allowing us to insert several players deeper than our first two units.

After this one, the players hoisted Jing off the floor on their shoulders, letting their good luck charm cut the net off the rim—an American basketball custom the U.S. players made known to their Chinese teammates. Hu's camera's soaked it up.

So, what was the difference in the two outings? Apparently, as Charley explained to me, it was simple: Don't panic.

"I never, ever saw a team get as hot as that little Eureka team," he explained to me back on our campus. "Even their coach, a nice guy by the way, told me the same thing afterward.

"So that's what I told our kids. Shake it off. It was a fluke. Don't panic. Hang in there. Never mind I was peeing in my pants."

Now it was off to Fargo and the sectional tournament in the North Dakota Beef Processors Arena—another slice of Americana for our Chinese friends.

New turf to me, too.

CHAPTER

92

Outside help

DODGE CITY IN Kansas was Mesquite's next stop on the NCAA trail. Billy Jack arrived with much on his mind.

Naturally there were the Xs and Os that came with strategizing against opponents. Though confident every game was winnable, after all the Buckaroos were the second-ranked team in the entire field, the competition got stronger with each contest.

The Buckaroos would be matched against Nebraska-Red Cloud, a branch of Nebraska University in Lincoln and a ranked team most of the season. If successful, they would advance to play the winner of Greeley College (Colo.) vs. Northwest Texas State.

Each school, unlike Mesquite, had made an NCAA tournament appearance within the last three years. The Buckaroos were unimpressed, however. Their backgrounds—Iraq vet, East LA, Islamic convert, Texas prison, and God knew what else with Oscar and Pete—made them a salty crew.

A growing concern for the coaches was J.J. Someone might recognize him as Jumbo and, putting pieces together (most likely a snoopy opposing coach), suspect something wasn't right.

The team was drawing more and more scrutiny with each game. There would be real reporters covering this tournament.

Worse, the NCAA required new, more detailed player biographies with each win. Every form he completed about his star player was fraudulent. Talk about leaving a paper trail!

Uppermost in Billy Jack's mind now, however, was the letter from the Clerk of Court's office in Chicago that Ollie handed him. The player showed it on the day the team left for Dodge City.

This was the official notice of Ollie's appearance before a judge in Cook County district court. It was scheduled for Friday next week, the day the Final Four opening games in Wintrust Arena also were scheduled.

"Look at this, Jimmy," Billy Jack said to his assistant. "He's got to be in front of a judge a week from Friday at 9. The first semifinal game, the one we'll be playing if we survive, starts at 12:15. You're from Chicago. You know the city. How far is the arena from the criminal court building?"

"Never had to make that trip. Traffic's always a bitch in Chicago, though."

The key was to find a good lawyer, they agreed.

The best-case scenario, Jimmy pointed out, was that the charges—disturbing the peace, resisting arrest— would get tossed. Quickly, and first thing in the morning.

Next best would be a continuation, in which case they could hustle from the courtroom to the basketball court in time for tipoff.

At worst, Jimmy added, was the charges got upheld, a court date set, and, to avoid incarceration, bail would need to be continued—a bureaucratic process that could delay arrival for any game.

"Yep, coach, better get a lawyer."

93

On the case

RANDY LARUE'S SOLO law firm occupied one room in a large office building on LaSalle Street in the heart of Chicago's financial district. He shared a secretary with a pool of three attorneys. The modest surroundings belied his successful practice.

For those in the know, he was one of the city's most effective go-to criminal defense attorneys. We're not talking cases that drew grand-standing public figures and TV cameras. No, his clients were those who wished to avoid the spotlight and, with reputations at stake, paid big bucks to do so.

He was a master at avoiding media glare, whether it was by behind-the-scenes plea bargains, venue changes, charges dismissed before adjudication, or, if all else failed, misdirecting journalists.

If he was part of a case considered a "heater" and getting headlines, always he was in the second or third chair of the defense team and almost never in the photo ops. There was future business to be gained in these lesser roles, too.

Randy, or "Lash" as pals called him, built his law practice and sizable bank account working both sides of the street. Fresh from law school, he took a job in the Cook County Public Defenders' office before, two years later, jumping ship to work in the county prosecutor's office.

His favorite story: As an assistant district attorney, he once put away an armed robber for 10 years; a year earlier as a public defender, he kept the same guy from being convicted of a previous armed robbery.

"I got 'em coming and going," he joked with friends.

Then, in the salad, siren-chasing days on his own in private practice, he prowled court corridors looking for clients. He did well, but he wasn't exactly the Lincoln Lawyer portrayed in Michael Connelly novels. He drove a beat-up Volkswagen.

Randy eventually hit the jackpot helping a powerful, local Congressman's son beat a DUI rap. Better yet—he kept it out of the newspapers.

From that point on, the city's top pols brought to him a steady flow of dirty laundry, cases that needed to be kept quiet and in front of friendly, eye-winking judges. By then, he was driving a Lexus.

No one knew the way around the massive Cook County Criminal Court building better than Randy "Lash" LaRue. Seemingly he was on a first name basis with every courthouse employee, from janitors to judicial clerks. They were al on his Christmas gift list.

When the phone rang and rang that weekday morning, his feet were on his desk, tie loosened, jacket strewn over a chair, and he was reading The Chicago Tribune sports pages and drinking coffee.

He did not answer it. Ordinarily the secretary he shared would've picked it up, but she was on break.

That was OK. Let the caller go to voice mail. Don't directly pick up the phone. Don't make them think you're anxious for clients. He never lost business with that philosophy.

Two hours later after returning the telephone call, Randy was quite glad that he connected. As a result, he could hear a cash register ringing in the distance.

The caller, a man named Harold "Big Hal" Mason, was phoning from Houston. "I know nothing about Chicago, but I'm told by those who should know you're the best at this sort of thing," said the voice with the broad Texas drawl.

This was music to Randy's ears. Forty-five minutes later, following a detailed explanation surrounding Ollie Maddox's arrests and potential court conflict in next week's NCAA basketball tournament, an agreement was struck.

For a one-time $10,000 fee, the lawyer guaranteed the Mesquite player would not miss tipoff in the Wintrust Arena no matter the case's final disposition. If necessary, he would personally drive the basketball player to, or from, the facilities.

Everything was predicated on Mesquite winning two more games to get into the Final Four, of course. If it failed to get out of Dodge City, the lawyer got $5,000 for his time.

Randy envisioned no problems. Easy money either way.

First, he'd get to the assigned courtroom's clerk—and he'd worked with this person before—to schedule the case for 9 a.m. at the top of the docket. This ensured a quick exit.

The ideal tactic was to get a continuation. This was easy enough on anyone's first appearance, and bail money already posted meant Ollie was free to leave in lieu of a new date.

Entering a "not guilty" plea, meaning a trial date needed to be set, had the same effect. This was just the arraignment, something that seemed to be lost on the Houston caller. This option, like the first, would mean extra billing for Big Hal to cover.

Get to the arena in time? Hell, he probably could arrange for a Chicago police escort, if it came to that.

Meanwhile, Randy would look for a way to get the arrests tossed on a technicality. This was one of his specialties. There always was some screwup in paperwork.

In a way, this would be fun.

The lawyer was a big sports fan. He played football for a small college before moving to Chicago to enroll in night school law classes. He was not aware the NCAA Division III's basketball Final Four was coming to town, but, now that he knew, probably would attend.

But there was more.

Over a decade ago, before success with the Congressman's son, he hired out part-time to do investigative work for the NCAA. This meant finding proof of rule violations by several Midwestern universities, who eventually received stiff penalties.

Today the NCAA has a full-time compliance task force, but in those days the association's enforcement office was woefully understaffed. Outsourcing cases to eager, young attorneys to investigate was common practice.

When assignments dried up, he came to realize there was much left for a lawyer to harvest in college sports. This Mesquite development might be a fortuitous re-entry point.

His past work gave him excellent knowledge of NCAA rules. Unknowingly or not, he knew how easy they could be broken. The regulations took up more space than the Chicago phonebook.

For instance, the caller from Houston—the guy who hired him to represent Ollie—had just violated a biggie. It was illegal for an outside booster of a school to independently pick up the legal fee for a student-athlete.

Lash smiled after he hung up his phone. He was very glad he took the call. This Mesquite crew could be worth watching, a dream client if there were more like Big Hal.

Or, as he often joked to peers when a good client came his way: "There could be gold in them 'thar' hills."

SCHOOL WAS IMPOSSIBLE on the Harrison campus in the week leading to the Sweet 16. Basketball dominated conversations.

The Colonials were two wins away from Chicago and Final Four. Everyone wanted a piece of the team. They were rock stars, and this confused the Chinese players who—their height withstanding—had tried to remain anonymous as possible.

Wang Chen, the star throughout the season as well the key to avoiding that embarrassing upset against Eureka, was the most popular attraction. At 6-11, he was hard to miss on the campus and around town.

The community crawled with journalists, and not just Hu and his crew. Sports Illustrated gave us a good shot on our Paducah showing. Now Sally Garcia, the SI writer who put us on the cover to start the whole media blitz, was back on the beat and prowling town.

Two SI cover spreads? Unthinkable.

Charley tried to shelter his squad from the excitement. He closed practice sessions, a first for Harrison.

Nate, by now our de facto security chief, posted his sternest Holy Rollers at every Miller Fieldhouse entrance to guarantee privacy. "No rough stuff, though, Pilgrim," he promised me.

No one could recall a small college getting attention like this from national media, let alone local outlets. An American school with five starters from China winning the NCAA basketball championship? With a cabbage—Jing—as some sort of talisman?

C'mon. What news organization could resist?

"This is crazy," said Mary. "I can't keep students on topic. Might as well be spring break. Except we're going north, to Fargo."

Between helping with tournament details and regular teaching duties, we'd seen very little of each other. She broached the idea of importing a soccer team from Mexico, or some Central American nation.

Later, dear. Kind of busy now.

Even grumpy traditionalists like Dean Brunk got caught in the wave. This was Indiana, after all, and basketball ruled. He called classes off in mid-week. At 900 miles, Fargo in North Dakota was not exactly a stone's throw from campus.

Charley flew ahead with the team, but, amazingly, the caravan to Fargo—without team buses—was as long as the Paducah trek. The Holy Rollers again ran interference.

About halfway to North Dakota the plan called for our motorized parade to swell more in numbers. A rendezvous was planned— somewhere in southern Wisconsin—with four buses of our Chinatown followers.

This was scheduled by Willy Wong, who couldn't get enough of us. "We love you guys," he said. "You get to Chicago, I can be big help. I know city inside and out," he said.

He handed me four U.S.-based Chinese language newspapers that carried front-page stories on our team. "This is huge for us," he said. "We are big newspaper readers unlike Americans. Everyone in our community is excited."

The Harrison crowd welcomed the Chicago contingent. Friendships sprouted, but obviously there were cultural differences to be bridged. For, sure something got lost in translation in the— odd? amusing?— messages on banners unfurled by the Chinese on sides of their buses.

"Challenge the foe!!"

"Be heroic"

"Overcome the opponent!!"

"The cabbage will prevail!!"

"Slay the dragon!!"

Willy, ever the entrepreneur, left no bases untouched after we won in Paducah. He secured NCAA permission for Chicago's Chinese-language radio station, KCHI-AM, to broadcast remaining tournament games.

It would be very helpful, he hinted, if I could help get the iconic filmmaker Hu as a halftime guest.

"Good for ratings," he said. "He so big in China. There is much interest in our community that he is here and interested in our basketball team. This is a reason why our newspapers are excited, too."

"We may have to work fast to get him on the radio, Willy," I informed. "You got to understand: There is no guarantee we will win our first game. Each opponent gets tougher. One loss and it's over. Poof."

The tournament was down to 16 colleges. Anything could happen. The experts thought the four teams assigned to the Fargo sectional comprised the most-balanced field.

The top-seeded team in our group, but not by much, was Badlands College of South Dakota. This was our first-round opponent. North-field College in Minnesota played Wisconsin-Monroe in the other game—with winners meeting to see who advanced to the Final Four.

Harrison and its two-platoon, international lineup was the main attraction. Mostly we were regarded as a novelty.

Could a team with five imported starters from China win an NCAA basketball championship? And, as it developed, would we have any Chinese players?

When I left my Durham Hall office to join the Fargo-bound caravan, Anne Waller, Dean Brunk's administrative assistant, ran up to me as I got into my car in the campus parking lot.

"This is for you, and it looked important," she said. "Glad I caught you. The call came from Chicago."

The note said to call Palmer Pratt, administrator, Midwest Region, U.S. Immigration & Customs Enforcement (ICE) Services. It was a Chicago number.

CHAPTER

95

Uh oh

THE FARGO-BOUND FAN bus was warming up in the Harrison parking lot. Mary knew something was askew the second I plopped down beside her.

What's wrong, she asked? After explaining I just got off the phone with Immigration in Chicago, her instant response was: "Damn. Can't be good."

It wasn't. My call to Palmer Pratt, a regional compliance officer, went unlike clockwork. I was put on hold for nearly 5 minutes, sitting through some of the most Godawful *muzak*. It got worse.

The replay:

"Mr. Doyle? Phillip J. Doyle," he asked.

Immediately I knew this was trouble. He used my full name. Yes.

"I understand you, as a representative of Harrison College, are the sponsor of 12 students from China," he said. "Is that correct?"

Yes.

"Well, I'm sorry to inform you, but we have a problem that will require immediate attention."

What?

"We have a deportation issue. There's been a mix-up, I've been informed. Papers are not in order. In effect, this is officially a matter of illegal immigration."

I tried to sound calm. Pratt softened a bit as he continued.

He explained that he followed the publicity surrounding Harrison's basketball journey. He understood timing was unfortunate, but the issue was out of his hands.

"But," he said, "this only concerns one student. It shouldn't impact the team," he said.

One?

"Yes, a Miss Jingfei Yong."

Jing? Our good luck charm? The cabbage? No way. We might as well lose Wang Chen. This was horrible news, both for Jing and the team. Everyone would be devastated. Forget basketball.

Pratt explained the pressure for her return was not coming from the U.S. It came from Beijing.

"We've had cases like this pop up lately," he continued. "Our Chinese counterparts are not forthcoming in details. But each time, it was a female declared in violation of regulations. At our end, we suspect it has to do with the 'missing girls'—the millions who are undocumented. Are you aware of this issue?"

Was I aware? This was it, of course. We thought simply getting Jing here meant we were OK.

Apparently, China bureaucracy caught up with us. Her parents, Zei and Li, undoubtedly were crushed at their end—if they even knew of this development.

The news got worse.

"The Chinese move quickly on these matters," said Pratt. "They expect her to report to their consulate offices Thursday next week in Chicago, packed and ready. I'll inform them we made contact."

This was the day before the Final Four opened in Chicago. Provided we made it that far, we had to give up our heart and soul. Morale would hit rock bottom. We needed a strategy, and quick.

Pratt became sympathetic as I explained exactly what Jing's loss meant. To the team? Heck, what it meant to the college. She had become an ambassador-of-good-will on the campus and in the community, making dozens of friends in the process.

He had no idea how the deportation could be stalled, let alone nixed altogether. "I've never heard of that happening and I cannot, or anyone

in our department, get involved. Ask around. Maybe you know someone
with connections in the counsel office here. That's my suggestion."

Mary and I huddled in the back of the bus, quietly. We wanted to
keep a lid on things for now while we thrashed out the new dilemma.
She knew immigration officials in the Southwest, but that was for
Mexico border issues. This was new territory. She knew no one in
Chicago, let alone anyone in the Chinese consulate.

I placed a quick, hushed cellphone call to President Casey, who
agreed to alert others in our inner circle. He said to keep him briefed on
progress.

For now, that would be it. Tomorrow, we'd alert Charley and then
decide what—if anything—to tell the team and Zhang, her brother. The
players would be crushed.

I'd let Jing know the situation soon after we got to Fargo. Mary
would join me in delivering the news. This figured to be emotional.
She'd made a great adjustment. Everyone loved her.

Undoubtedly Jing and I both would lean on Mary for support. We'd
been through a lot together. The dinner with her family in Xiamen
remained a highlight for me.

The challenge was to work angles to keep Jing in school until the
end of the academic year. She was earning A's in every course. She
deserved to finish a school year only weeks away. After all, this was the
plan that was officially approved.

By the time we hit Chicago on the fan bus, we'd worked out a variety
of scenarios and contingencies. We groped. It was too late at night to
make calls. Neither of us came up with anything solid anyway, aside
from trying to find someone familiar with the embassy's inner workings.

Deep into Wisconsin and chilly darkness, our caravan pulled off
Interstate 94 somewhere between Madison and Black River Falls. The
Flying J Travel Plaza, which offered a full range of gut-busting food
choices, was the scheduled rendezvous with the Chinatown convoy.

We got there first. Twenty minutes later, four buses from Chicago
pulled into the parking lot. We were joined by Willy Wong and his
Chinatown entourage to form what had to be the largest multi-national
caravan in the history of college hoops.

"This an easy sell for me," he said. "There are six casinos in Fargo. Six!! We love to watch our people play basketball; we love casino trips, too."

96

Hello, Chicago

NATURALLY, OLLIE PLAYED like a man possessed for Mesquite in Dodge City. It was as if he thought the performances could exonerate him in his Chicago court appearance. "Get me the ball," he said repeatedly in huddles.

The first game against Nebraska-Red Cloud was no contest from the opening toss. The Buckaroos ran off a 12-0 start, with Ollie getting eight points and three rebounds in the spurt. He finished with a season high 36 points and 19 rebounds in what turned out to be a 102-77 rout.

Indispensable was the best description, but that only made Billy Jack wary. What if they made it to the Final Four and his star forward was in the slammer and not available?

He was a force in Game No. 2, too. In this one Mesquite ran past Northwest Texas State 89-80—giving the Oklahoma Panhandle school its first-ever Final Four appearance.

Typically, the team's most stoic player, Ollie stood at half-court at the final buzzer with his outstretched, heavily tattooed arms held high above his head. For a full 45 seconds, he repeatedly yelled: "We showed 'em!! We showed 'em!! Nobody's stoppin' us."

Oscar and Ollie used the two games to perfect a new Spanish-language play, "*Puerta trasera cuatro*"—a backdoor move in which the power forward faked in one direction, then, in a few giant strides, launched himself high above the rim to jam home a teammate's lob pass.

Until these games, Maddox wanted little to do with Oscar's Spanish-language playmaking innovations. His new-found, "born again" attitude knew no bounds.

The Buckaroos stormed the floor. Billy Jack allowed himself to celebrate, too, despite the cloud that hung over his team. After all, he was one step closer to the NCAA championship and, a Waco State feeler withstanding, Division I job opportunities.

Even Merrilou could not contain herself. In addition to the basketball team advancing to the Final Four, her cheerleaders were headed to Chicago with a dual purpose.

They would cheer the Buckaroos, but they also advanced in competition that was a first-time event for the NCAA. If they won in the next round against the other three squads in the Final Four, this earned a spot on the local Fox-TV morning show in Chicago.

"Can you believe this, honey?" she said, after they walked through the door of their spacious Amarillo condo. "This could be a double victory for us. I am sooo happy you talked me into coaching cheerleaders."

While the team bussed from Dodge City to Beaver Junction, a distance of only 100 miles, Big Hal and Ruthie dropped their daughter and son-in-law off at Amarillo in a chartered, small jet before zipping on to Houston.

Big Hal's parting words were music to Billy Jack's ears: See you two lovebirds in Chicago and don't worry about a thing. I've got Ollie's situation taken care of. I'll get details to you tomorrow. Enjoy yourselves."

Good thing her parents did not stay.

Merrilou was eager to show her husband just how happy she was over developments. Unpacking had to wait. Undressing, not so much.

CHAPTER

97

Rally time

TO TELL THEM, or not to tell them? That was the question.

We left it up to Charley about how to handle the breaking Jing news with his Harrison team before our Fargo opener. Did he want them to know before we met Badlands College? Or, did he wish to do it afterward? If we lost, after all, it was moot as far as basketball went.

"I can't keep it from them," said Charley. "I have to treat my players like adults. They have to meet challenges on and off the floor. We love Jing, but they need to respond like adults. They've come too far, worked too hard for this."

Also, Charley asked us to keep this backstory from the media as best we could. It would do Jing no good and, from a selfish standpoint, he did not want any hint the team's fortunes rose and fell because of a good luck charm. Who could argue?

Of course, Jing was crushed when Mary and I broke the news to her in the hotel lobby. She never expected to remain in the U.S. beyond the school year, though we knew it wasn't out of the question there might be ways to extend the stay.

We promised to do everything possible to delay deportation. President Casey, who agreed to keep our inner circle abreast of developments, gave us his full support to pursue a solution. "I don't want to know the details," he quickly added. For his own protection, of course.

Perhaps the worst part for Jing was this: What did she face in a return to China? Would she become consigned to second-class status and denied future opportunities? Would this episode cause problems for her parents? Or brother, Zhang?

Always upbeat until now, her sad face and tears were a first for me since I first met her at Xiamen University. She had become important to me. Now close to realizing a dream, then—poof! Our vows to do what we could brought a smile, but her teary, brown eyes remained sad.

Our options were long-shots and, well, frivolous in some instances: Call our Congressman (whoever that was); flee to Canada; file paperwork with the Chinese consul to delay (probably too late); adopt her (too late for that, too); or simply don't have her report Thursday, surely a crime.

Before the first-round game in Fargo's North Dakota Beef Processors Arena, Jing addressed the Colonials. She made them promise to win this sectional while she remained—and, then, go all the way in Chicago without their good luck charm. They could do it.

She brought a gift for them to take to the Final Four without her: An inflatable, toy cabbage as her replacement. They could place it on the bench for "good luck."

There was much sadness when the pre-game meeting was over. Everyone gave Jing a hug as they left the locker room.

Badlands College never had a chance in our opener, 92-78. It was total team effort. The first-unit Pandas put the game almost out of reach by halftime. The second-unit Eagles, led by more amazing Jimmy Bradley shooting, played almost the entire second half.

Later it occurred to me why Charley wanted the Eagles on the floor so long. This would strengthen cohesion if Harrison made it to Chicago, where it was impossible to gauge how the Pandas would react without Jing—the toy cabbage notwithstanding.

In fact, in another of Charley's moves, he next started the Eagles in the sectional final contest against a rangy University of Wisconsin-Monroe team that upset Northfield College in its semifinal. He did this only once before during the season.

The Cheesemakers (what else?) from Wisconsin were thoroughly baffled. By the time they figured counters, our faster-moving Pandas came roaring off the bench determined to outperform their Harrison teammates. They played with anger. Yang got whistled for four fouls, unusual for him.

UW-Monroe, which could match our height, staged a comeback, pulling to an 81-78 deficit with little more than a minute left. By then it had a 22-8 edge in free throws thanks to our excessive fouling.

Charley ran the Eagles back on the court at this point. Because they were better ballhandlers than the Pandas, the Colonials outlasted the rally.

The unthinkable had happened: Harrison College, the school named for the most obscure president in U.S. history and which never knew real athletic success, was headed for the men's Final Four in Chicago. And we owed it to five players named Chen, Yang, Yong, Li, and Lu.

If this didn't rate another Sports Illustrated cover, what did? At the final buzzer the players rushed to Jing and, carrying her on their shoulders, took a victory lap around the court.

The festivities got transferred to the team's hotel lobby. The pep band that played during the game re-assembled to add music—loud music—to the partying.

President Casey was in the middle of the post-game celebration, high-fiving and fist-bumping everyone in sight. Our new Chinatown pals from Chicago added a nice touch, too. Pretty sure the good folks of Fargo who wandered into the festivities were impressed.

We paid a price the next morning, of course. Mary and I, like most everyone, got little sleep. Our heads pounded, and we had work ahead: Was there a way to get Jing's deportation nixed?

There was little time. Like, by next Thursday. This was Sunday.

As it turned out we were surrounded by a possible solution. Everything crystallized for me by the time we pulled into that Black River Falls' Flying J Travel Plaza on Interstate 94 on the return trip.

We used this again as a rendezvous spot for our convoy, which, despite the Holy Rollers' best efforts to keep us together, became scattered. It took a half-hour or so for everyone to gather. The straggling buses, eight including Chinatown's four entries, finally were at one end of the parking lot while all other vehicles took the remaining spaces.

Up to that point, Mary and I had sat in the back of our bus working on Jing's deportation problem. A few calls were made, and one to Jeanne Martin—our well-connected communications person—for advice. Even she was at a loss.

My sympathies lied totally with Jing and her dreams of attending an American college. Couldn't the basketball team win without her—good luck icon or not? A thousand things were going through my brain. I popped aspirins as my headache grew.

Mary didn't need them when I offered to share. Either she did not drink as much or had stronger cognitive powers. My money was on the latter, and this became obvious about a half-hour before the Flying J.

"You know," she finally pointed out, "we're sitting here trying to figure a solution for Jing when we are surrounded by the solution."

"How so? All I see is dairy cows and farms outside, and hungover Harrison fans in our bus."

"No, silly. We're surrounded by Chinese. Several hundred of them in the other buses we're about to link up with. Every person in Willy Wong's crowd probably dealt with immigration matters in Chicago. We're looking at the forest, but they're the trees. Let's ask them for help."

Duhhh.

This, of course, meant a straight line to the bus carrying Willy "Can do" Wong. When it pulled into the Flying J parking lot, I was there at its door to greet him. When he exited, I stuck out my hand, shook his, and said: "Willy. Have I got a job for you."

"Bring it on," he quickly replied.

Showdown in Chicago

Making plans

THE MEN'S FINAL Four for small colleges does not receive Big Tent attention. No live TV, either, unless it's one of those channels buried deep in a cable package or Internet-only. In most newspapers, the results rate a line or two.

The championship typically is decided in small markets. Better to be a big frog in a little pond like Grand Rapids, Mich., or Johnson City, Tenn., the NCAA reasoned. These communities roll out red carpets. Free rooms, meals, and loaner cars for tournament officials. No problem. Y'all come back.

Chicago and its new Wintrust Arena on the lakefront? Now this was big-time. It was a gamble that looked better and better to NCAA officials as our Final Four approached.

With the Chicago Bulls dead meat, and local universities DePaul, Loyola, and Northwestern stuck in sand—and the Cubs weeks from Opening Day, local print media like the Tribune, Sun-Times, and Daily Herald paid attention. They sent reporters and columnists.

The TV stations, typically taking a cue from print, followed suit.

A novelty for Chicago? For sure, but by tipoff time everyone wanted to see the little college—Henderson? Harris? Garfield? Whatever it was— with the Chinese players.

Sports Illustrated set the table for that, of course, with more coverage. But Harrison withstanding, in my book it was a colorful field filled with good storylines that assembled for the showdown.

Our first opponent was No. 1 ranked Milton College of Massachusetts, the defending champion. The school was named for poet John Milton, author of *"Paradise Lost."* Supposedly it had a bang-up English department. Naturally its sports teams were called the Poets.

A Milton win over us, not totally unexpected since we were the Final Four's bottom seed, might produce—to me—a classic matchup. The Poets could play Stratford College if both won their semifinal contests.

Stratford was a surprise entry like Harrison, pulling off several major upsets to get to Chicago. The team was built around a Sudanese center, Hassan el Khalifa. He was, at 7-foot-3, a very compelling person who, by all accounts, could do more on a basketball court than walk and chew gum at the same time.

The school was in Ashland, Ore., located in the far southwest corner of the state and home of a well-known, annual Shakespeare Festival. Its sports teams were called the Bards.

So why would a Stratford vs. Milton matchup be classic? Hey, it would be Poets vs. Bards for the NCAA title! If I covered the contest, the story would write itself.

Of course, Stratford would need to beat another Final Four first-timer in Mesquite College, which came out of nowhere—figuratively and literally—in Oklahoma.

I did not know much about these guys, but they were undefeated like Milton. I did learn it had a good rodeo program and they were called the Buckaroos. Also, Mesquite was the only Final Four school to have its cheerleaders in the finals, too.

Poets, Bards, Buckaroos, and Colonials. Loved it. Wildcats, Spartans, Cardinals, Buckeyes, Bruins? Yawn.

The official Final Four hotels were the Palmer House and Conrad Hilton, short rides from the arena. The semifinals were Friday and Sunday, and the teams assembled on Wednesday. Some of us arrived earlier with much on our minds.

In addition to Wintrust practice sessions, a variety of events and sites were lined up for tournament participants to help generate hype.

This included a Bulls game in the United Center against the Indiana Pacers, who were very popular with us. The Pacers were watching when Harrison beat Indiana State in Indianapolis to get on the national map. This seemed a century ago.

The NCAA arranged a ceremonial appearance in City Hall, where team captains posed with the Chicago mayor during the reading of a proclamation welcoming the tournament to town. This was awkward. The shortest player at the podium was at least a foot taller than the diminutive mayor.

The scheduled outdoor events mostly got scratched. Hey, it was March in Chicago. This meant rain, cold, and always the possibility for snow. Who planned that Chicago boat ride, anyway?

Some Harrison players, led by the inquisitive Chinese, visited the Art Institute of Chicago. They were interested in seeing the Taoist Tradition exhibit. Several were doing a paper on it for class. Pretty sure a visit to the art institute was a first for any basketball team visiting the Windy City.

When the Harrison contingent first assembled in Chicago before its opener, I already had been there two days "working the streets." Well, it was not quite that colorful, but I was on the case for Jing.

Time was running short. She arrived with the team on Wednesday, baggage in hand, and was to report the next day—Thursday—to the Chinese consulate, located in the River North area not far from the downtown Loop and our Palmer House hotel.

I was new to this, but my understanding was that she would be sent back to China after necessary paperwork and a de-briefing. If the flight was not that day, the consulate put her up in hostel-like accommodations it maintained for citizens in "transition" until another flight was available.

Could Willy Wong save the day? He indicated as much when Mary and I told him the problem at the Wisconsin plaza. I gave him every detail, starting with my Xiamen teaching experience. He appeared sympathetic.

"I know about these things, when my people have problems," he said. "This happens much. There are things I can do to help. There is not much time to fix this. Do you want me be legal or not so legal?"

Errr, we'll leave that up to you. When in Rome, etc., etc.

Willy got to know Jing well in little time with us, starting in Paducah at the start of our tournament odyssey. "She nice," he said, "and she could be big help with radio (KCHI) broadcasts during games. Let me see what I can do for her. I know people in the consulate. Often they eat at my Chinatown restaurant."

On Monday, my calls to Willy for a status report went unanswered. I left voicemails, but heard nothing in response. This made me nervous.

On Tuesday morning, I took an Uber to Chinatown to the Chamber of Commerce office to hopefully get from him a personal status report.

This was my first-ever visit to the neighborhood, and I promised myself to bring Mary here someday when things settled. There was maybe a half-mile square of shops, restaurants, Internet cafes, food marts, book stores, temples and other specialty businesses catering to its ethnic market.

The bright colors and architecture—curved and peaked roofs, small green parks, cobblestoned busy alleys, courtyards as public gathering spots—made me think I was in Xiamen.

I found the C of C office on the second level pedway on a side street off the main avenue, Confucius Way. Willy was in and working his telephones.

"Ah, I was just about to call you," he said. "Welcome to my world. I have news. Good or bad? I do not know. We see."

On Wednesday, the next day, he told me that he arranged for several key Chinese consulate case workers to come to his restaurant named—and I am not making this up—Willy Wong's Wonderful Wok for lunch. They were old, but familiar, contacts he'd conducted unspecified business with before, he added.

They wanted to talk about this matter away from their office, where it was likely they could be overheard and telephones were tapped. Also, they loved his pork dumplings.

What kind of business did you do with them, I asked.

He answered, "Ah, how you say in English?"

He paused, then said with a big smile: "Don't ask, don't tell. That's it. I love that saying. Don't ask, don't tell."

Turned out his consulate contacts had the power to create a "new residency status" for Jing, which for now meant temporary relief from deportation. Their recommendations would be reviewed by a superior, who generally—not always—rubber stamped their petitions.

This would delay any action, including the immediate return flight to China. The Chinese government was not interested in spending more money than necessary on flights. She could stay in the U.S. until a final disposition was made, which likely could be dragged out to the end of the school term.

"There is no guarantee," Willy added, "but they know about the basketball team. Like many in Chicago, they are quite excited. I tell them about Jing's connection. They help.

"Oh. We need to get tickets to them to Final Four. Big demand for them among China community. Very hot."

Well, that was no problem. Hell, I could get them seated in President Casey's lap if they wished.

Best case scenario: Jing would get to finish the school term, and perhaps stay in the U.S. beyond that May date.

It could be a nail-biter, though. Jing, who would be brought up to speed beforehand, needed to keep her Thursday appointment.

Worst case scenario: There remained a possibility she would be on a flight as soon as Thursday night headed for Beijing.

"You need to—how you say?—sit tight," said Willy. "Hope for good things. Say a prayer. Burn a candle. I sell them, by the way."

Fast getaway?

THE MESQUITE ENTOURAGE arrived at the Conrad Hilton Hotel on Wednesday with Jimmy in charge. Billy Jack arrived 24 hours earlier.

The coach, a stickler for detail, wanted a feel for logistics. This meant a tour of the Cook County Criminal Courts Building before a short meet with attorney Randy LaRue, arranged in advance by Big Hal.

He discovered the courthouse deciding Ollie's fate to be a huge, gray stone building fronted by tall, round columns. There was a constant stream of humanity through the entry doors as well as cars and buses with wire-mesh covered windows using driveways to rear entrances.

The squat-looking building was built in the 1920s, a bit of an architectural marvel at the time. Now it was in need of sandblasting—or whatever they do to brighten stone exteriors. The location was in Chicago's dense, Near Southwest side at the corner of 26th Street and California Avenue. The neighborhood, mostly Hispanic, was known as Little Village.

On one side of the courthouse was a taller, modernistic steel and glass building. This was home to offices for judges, prosecutors, corporate counsels, administrative assistants, and several divisions of the sheriff's department as well as other enforcement agencies.

Across California Avenue, completing a local triumvirate for justice, was the Cook County Jail occupying nearly 100 acres and housing close to 7,000 inmates. Also, there was a vegetable garden maintained by the most trusted inmates.

If Ollie had been unable to post bail, this would've been his residence—guilty or innocent—until his upcoming, Friday, court date. No telling how he would've survived incarceration. He was a tough kid, but not that tough.

The immediate commercial neighborhood had a half-dozen small offices offering bail services, two pawn shops, one Dunkin Donuts, one Taco Bell, and a Popeye's Chicken.

After a thorough pat down by grim-faced, pistol-packing security personnel and x-rays that could detect a hangnail, Billy Jack quickly got swept up by purposeful-looking, noisy foot traffic in courthouse hallways.

Most conspicuous were uniformed deputies escorting handcuffed defendants to court rooms. Many were marched to the building through a tunnel that connected the jail with the courthouse. Others arrived by bus—in cuffs—from satellite jails spread throughout the county.

Lawyers seemed to be everywhere. Billy Jack admired their suits. Many huddled with clients, in some cases joined by fearful-looking, anxious family members. Others worked their cell phones.

The coach had a plan for this visit. He found a court room on the top floor that was, according to his calculations, about as far as one could get from the building's entrance.

Carefully noting the time, he quickly strode down the stairsteps and back through the main entrance to the street to make a link—it took 6 minutes total—with a parked taxi.

"Take me to the Wintrust Arena and make it as direct and quick as possible," the coach said to the driver. By the time they arrived at the giant, new sports facility sitting on Lake Michigan, the entire exercise took nearly 57 minutes in what seemed to the coach to be moderate traffic.

Later, in attorney Randy LaRue's office, Billy Jack got right to the point as soon as he took a seat for their meeting.

"How the hell is this going to work? Our game starts in Wintrust at Noon—12:05 to be exact—and his court appearance is at 9. I need him at least a half-hour before tipoff for God's sake. Doesn't look to me like you can do it."

Billy Jack went on to explain his visit to the courthouse earlier in the day, how he had timed the whole exercise, and what his taxi driver said—"50-50, mon"— about traffic patterns in Chicago.

This quickly became a classic, textbook matchup: A college basketball coach, in a profession where bullshit is a way of life, getting bullshitted by a totally-wired Chicago criminal defense attorney, whose whole livelihood revolved around making bad things sound good.

Too bad it wasn't taped.

It was no contest. Twenty minutes later, Randy had his new client calmed. Careful to not give away details of just how he could deliver Ollie in time, he gave a carefully-worded, but totally generic, explanation that seemed to defuse his visitor's concerns.

The truth was, the lawyer had no clue of how it could be done. While he did not doubt for a second the player would walk out a free and clear man, delivering him in time for the game was another matter.

And, even if he did have a specific plan, no way would he reveal it ahead of time. That wasn't the way he waged war in Chicago's legal battlefields. No matter how big the payday, he was not about to alter his style or reveal his tricks to anyone.

Billy Jack left with an impression everything was in good hands. And Randy? No way he would miss Big Hal's fat fee.

The lawyer also was savvy enough about sports to recognize what he saw in the well-coiffed Billy Jack: Stark ambition. He would not think twice about breaking rules to get to the top, a possible, future bonanza for his law practice.

ON THURSDAY, 24 hours before Final Four tipoff, the four teams and their official entourages were guests of honor at a luncheon organized by the Chicago Tourism Bureau. This included Mary and me.

Our NCAA tournament didn't have Division I stature, but a plush, red carpet awaited us. The mayor was on hand and stayed to the end. Joining him at the head table were the presidents of the schools, head coaches, Wintrust CEO, and various NCAA officials.

The emcee was an unctuous, local TV sportscaster whose name I forget—and who mispronounced at least half the players' names.

There also were several minor, elected officials, who, despite having nothing to do with the tournament, jockeyed for good spots in photo ops and managed to get acknowledged.

I mean the Cook County Recorder of Deeds? Really? Later, someone explained to me it was an election year.

Following introductions, the presidents of the schools each were limited to a minute's response. Our guy, President Casey, handled it well.

We were not favored to win, but everyone was curious about us. Our presence clearly attracted national media and turned the tournament into an "event."

After noting the presence of so many from the media in the room, Jonathan drew a big laugh with this: "I just hope all the press shows up the next time we dedicate a new building on our campus."

If we had a rival for attention, it was the Sudanese center for Stratford College, Hassan el Khalifa. Though 7-foot-3, he could not have weighed over 200 pounds.

Scouting reports said Khalifa could do more than walk and chew gum at the same time, too. Our Wang Chen, at 6-foot-11, would have his hands full if we met, which would have to be the title game.

This tournament was looking more global than the Olympics.

I did notice the president of Mesquite College wore cowboy boots and a string tie. I did not notice if he checked a cowboy hat before entering the room.

The Mesquite president's attire was in sharp contrast to his coach, whose charcoal gray, "Paul Smith" pinstriped suit cost at least two grand. (I Googled it during the program.) He certainly dressed like he was going places.

You always hold your breath at these events, wondering how students deport themselves. Will they wear low-riders with their ass-cracks on display? Tattoos creeping above collars? Baseball caps at 90-degree angles they never take off?

This was Division III and featured, as far as I knew, *real* student-athletes. Almost everyone wore sport coats and ties. The others wore sweaters. I spotted nothing outrageous with only one exception. One player in the Mesquite crew wore a tuxedo—a powder blue tuxedo, no less.

On the room's periphery, I saw Hu Jun and Maggie Wei directing their camera crews shooting the proceedings. They were present throughout our basketball odyssey, of course, but blended in like so much wallpaper.

They would have no shortage of film for a documentary. I was curious to see the final product. In my mind, and certainly President Casey's, this could be the real prize for Harrison College.

A billion Chinese becoming aware of our school? Eat your hearts out, Ivy League. Stanford, too.

If there was a concern about their project, it was this: They would discover our late-developing dilemma with Jing.

We did not wish to turn the Harrison narrative into something that could anger China's government. This could make things more difficult for Jing, her family, and cast our school in a bad light.

And speaking of Jing, I had my cellphone on during the entire University Club luncheon. I did not want to miss calls. She reported to the consulate bright and early that morning.

When our two-hour event concluded, I still had not heard anything from her. Was that good or bad news?

101

Let Games Begin

8:45 A.M., GAME DAY: Room 302, Cook County Criminal Courts Building, Chicago.

The basketball court seemed a hundred miles away. This was a real court, where "referees" wore black robes and cheering was not allowed.

Ollie, several cousins, and the storefront church pastor who originally arranged bail back in January, huddled with Randy LaRue. They were in the rear of the room and whispered.

"So, here's the deal," he told his attentive audience. "We got a friendly clerk who's put us first on the docket. I'm also sure we got a friendly judge, Judge Engel. I've dealt with him before. He's tough on cops."

Randy went over a few technicalities, outlining several scenarios. None involved incarceration. No matter. The lawyer was set to post necessary bail, which did not figure to be high.

The challenge, of course, was timing. If paperwork took more than 30 minutes, there would be problems getting to the game in time for the noon tipoff for Mesquite against Stratford.

"Ollie, you look scared," said Randy. "Don't be. You're sweating pretty heavy, son."

"I'm hot," said the Mesquite player. "I got my uniform on underneath."

He continued to sweat, but not due to proceedings in Room 302. They went like clockwork—if you used Randy's clock.

Turned out they were in front of Judge Engel a total of 2 minutes, 14 seconds. That's how long it took to discover paperwork not in order—something about a missing page—and the judge, eyeing a full docket and crowded courtroom, simply did not want to take time to look for it.

He tossed the charges. "You've never been in trouble like this before as far as I can see," said the judge. "Just stay out of trouble, young man. Next time you might not be so lucky. We're done. You're excused."

The assistant state's attorney, plus two cops ready to testify, were upset. They blustered, got cut off by the judge, and tromped down the aisle quietly cursing to themselves. As courthouse outbursts go, it rated about 2 on a scale of 10, with 10 the worst.

LaRue rushed his flabbergasted client from the courtroom before anything could be said. There was a quick, knowing glance exchanged between the lawyer and clerk unseen by anyone else that, to only the savvy insider, probably explained the mysterious missing page.

A Cook County sheriff's deputy met Randy and Ollie in the hallway. The deputy quickly escorted them into the elevator, but pushed the "up" button. No words were spoken.

After reaching the last stop, with the lawyer glancing at his wristwatch, they hurried down a hallway to a smaller, private elevator that required an ID card produced by the deputy. This took them one more flight to the building's top floor.

Then, showing his pass to security, they climbed a final stairway and exited out a doorway to the roof—where a Cook County sheriff's department helicopter was warming up on a small helipad.

The scheduled flight time to a the helipad atop McCormick Place, the giant, Chicago exhibition hall a few blocks from Wintrust, was 4 minutes and 24 seconds.

"Oh no, man, you never said anything about this," said Ollie, when he first saw the helicopter. "I don't like these things. They scare me, dude. I get sick. Did it once before. Puked, too."

Randy reached into the helicopter, grabbed an airsick bag, and handed it to the player and hurried him to a seat after they stepped aboard.

Bottom line: The entire exercise was breathtaking, a smooth, flawless coordination of public and private enterprise that would be the envy of the most efficient professional project manager. No money exchanged hands. The only "currencies" were IOUs, either collected or earned.

As the helicopter skimmed the Chicago rooftops with Ollie's face buried in the bag, Randy leaned back, clasped his hands behind his head, and took in the magnificent skyline.

He smiled. What a wonderful view, he thought to himself. Tourists would pay big for this experience. Maybe he should have billed a larger fee.

When the aircraft landed on the McCormick Place roof, two security persons for the exhibition hall were there to greet the attorney and his retching client. They whisked through a series of private elevators, which took them to the building's employee entrance.

Randy looked at his watch, saw they were five minutes ahead of schedule, and waved off a waiting car. "Let's walk it," he told Ollie. "It's only a few blocks to Wintrust. You can get your legs back, breathe some fresh air."

Amazingly, the player and his attorney arrived at the Wintrust Arena's player entrance before Billy Jack and the team. "Oh, wow, am I glad to see you," said the coach, embracing Ollie as if they hadn't seen each other for a year.

"This is just great," he said, shaking hands vigorously with Randy. "You said you could deliver and you did."

The Buckaroo entourage entered the arena, leaving the attorney thinking: Yep. I should've charged more.

102

Mesquite vs. Stratford

IT NEVER HURTS to have a 7-footer on your basketball team, whether or not he or she is good. That was Billy Jack's thinking when he recruited Luke Hodges, after first spotting him in line in a McDonald's just off I-90 in Murdo, S.D. It made no difference he never played high school basketball.

Pure and simple, the Mesquite coach simply wanted a 7-footer (in this case 7-foot-1 to be exact). Sooner or later, he knew this person could make a valuable contribution. Now was that time.

Hodges was not good enough to be a Mesquite starter, but, thanks to liberal play as a reserve, he was a passable ballhandler, fair shooter with very limited range, and decent rebounder.

These were not abilities his coach wanted from Luke in this game,

"I simply want him to go in there and hack the shit out of that big Sudanese," Billy Jack said to Jimmy. "We won't start Hodges, but we'll get him in real soon and often. I want their big guy looking over his shoulder every time Luke's on the floor."

Hassan el Khalifa experienced this strategy before, but this time there was a difference. Luke was just as tall—a rarity—and had a much longer reach than the previous stalkers. This forced the Stratford star to alter trajectories when he shot, a first-time experience.

The Sudanese beanpole tried moving farther from the basket. There, J.J. and Ollie, both excellent defensive players, swarmed him—though it did take Ollie, enfeebled from his helicopter ride, until midway in the first half to get into the contest's flow.

Hodges hounded el Khalifa, even when he did not have the basketball. He pushed. He shoved. He elbowed. Once, he stomped on his foot. He made the African work for everything.

Luke had no interest in scoring or rebounding, just applying pressure to Stratford's star. That was his coach's dictate. At least twice the opponents got into shoving matches and were separated by teammates before refs got involved.

In one collision, el Khalifa's nose got bloodied.

"Perfect, just perfect," Billy Jack muttered to Jimmy on the bench. "I knew there was a place for Luke."

The Buckaroo played as deep as he could get when his team had the basketball, the better to make his guy run the full length of the floor. When the Stratford star came off the floor, so did Hodges.

The strategy became obvious to the most casual spectator. When Hodges picked up his fourth foul, one shy of fouling out, Billy Jack defied conventional coaching wisdom. He kept his center in the contest simply because el Khalifa remained on the floor.

The contest was close. The capacity crowd was into it, big time.

Mesquite and Stratford never were separated by more than five points. The lead changed hands at least a dozen times before the inevitable happened—the Sudanese center ran out of gas.

Late in the game with just over 3 minutes remaining, the Bards coach took his star out for a rest—no more than 45 seconds ticked off the arena clock. That was enough time to make it obvious how much the Oregon school depended on him.

Mesquite rattled off six straight points, with the help of two steals by Buckaroo guard Mohammad Abdullah. These led to fast breaks finished by teammates Pete Dantley and J.J. This added up to an 8-point lead. Game over.

There would no Bards playing the Poets for the championship.

"We did it," said Billy Jack, in an emotional bear hug with Jimmy.

"We're in the finals."

Enthusiastic Mesquite followers jammed the court. The Buckaroo cheerleaders, whose upcoming competition was the next day, bounced around the happy scrum. Merrilou dashed from her box seat to join festivities.

Far up in a nosebleed seat, Randy LaRue smiled. As someone who knew his way around sports, he had a better understanding than anyone exactly what had transpired this day—from rescuing Ollie Maddox, Mesquite's leading scorer as it turned out, to the coach's do-what-it-takes strategy.

Yes. Billy Jack's career would bear watching, he thought.

Jing?

HARRISON VS. MILTON was not until 3:05 p.m. The Mesquite win that preceded it was exciting, but no question this second contest was the day's main event.

The Poets, undefeated and defending champion, against the Colonials, a Chinese lineup operating in a two-platoon system. Say what? Pass the fried rice, please.

Wintrust, with 12,000 seating capacity, was jammed for this semifinal unlike the first game that saw scattered, unoccupied seats. Tickets got scalped for this one, unheard of for an NCAA Division III event.

In a last-minute arrangement, ESPN pulled a "big foot" and secured broadcast rights to air the contest live. Its harried attempt to have tipoff moved 4 hours to prime time, a real headache for ticket holders and the dozen or so radio broadcasts, got nixed.

The Harrison tournament games were of interest to major college programs. Many had scouts following us since Paducah. They hoped to dangle full-ride scholarships to potential transfers they figured could be helpful to their programs.

Press row was packed. Willy Wong and his KCHI-AM radio crew had a courtside hookup, but with a vacant seat in its midst—Jing's.

Willy frowned when we made eye contact. Where was she? The appearance in the Chinese consulate was expected to be a formality. She went alone. The plan was to call me on her way via Uber to our game.

I would relay the news to Charley, whose players were anxious for their good luck charm to be present. I gave her until noon to call. Nothing.

Then, I started calling her—and each time was sent directly to voicemail. If she were a late arrival, her press credential allowed her to go straight to the KCHI-AM seat at courtside in full view of Harrison's bench.

To the outsider, this all probably sounded silly. A basketball team needed a good luck charm to win? Well, yes.

At least our Chinese players, from a country that had many superstitions, felt they needed the "cabbage." No Jing, no luck. You could see it in their faces. She was their symbol of good fortune. They were mostly teenagers, after all.

With tipoff moments away, Charley resigned himself. He gave a "win one for Jing" pep talk in the huddle.

Mary and I sat one row behind the Colonial bench, which meant I could coordinate a late arrival. She never showed.

Jing either was sitting in some detention area in the consulate office before whisked off to Beijing, or already was above us on a flight headed in that direction. We played the game without her.

Milton College was No. 1 ranked from the start of the season. The rating was owed in part to winning the national title the previous year. Also, its coach was very influential within NCAA circles.

Not every follower was convinced this year's Milton squad was strong as last year's team, which graduated three starters. There are many unknowns in the small college ranks. Pollsters favor familiar programs—until an unknown school proves differently.

We were a stranger in this promised land, regarded by hard core basketball junkies as a fluke. Meanwhile the Poets' quest for a repeat title was rare. It had a legendary coach, Lee Walters, a stoic, humorless fellow in his 31st year at Milton—his alma mater.

It's for sure Walters saw us as a fluke, some sort of Ebola germ that needed to be eradicated. A starting lineup comprised entirely of foreign transfer students? No way. This game was invented in America. He needed to prevent this germ from spreading.

If Walters knew our starters were troubled by something as silly (to him) as Jing's absence, he might have been tempted to change his deliberate, slow-down tactics. He'd have the Poets come out running, be aggressive. Kick us while we were down. At least that was my thinking.

With one eye out for Jing and the other on the game that unfolded, it became obvious I underestimated Charley. He continued to play on his players' emotions.

This worked. They got angry. The contest turned into a rout. After a slow start and an early timeout, in a rare display of temper, he chewed out his players and Harrison went on a 12-0 tear. They never looked back.

Both the Panda and Eagle units rolled as if they were trying to outdo each other. We led by 15 at halftime and won 93-72.

"I told them to forget everything surrounding the game. Just concentrate on the opponent," said Charley. "We were too good to fail. One way or another, she'd get the news. What did they want her to learn? That we lost?"

The outcome was a bitter pill for Walters, Milton's martinet coach. At mid-court he shook hands—stiffly—with Charley, whispered something in our guy's ear, and walked off.

"He just told me good luck," said Charley. "He also said let's schedule a game for next year. He knows our Chinese are gone then, the dick."

As if news could not get better, the morning after our huge victory Jing called. She was in the hotel lobby!

"I'm back, and we won and I'm so happy about this, and I can stay to the end of the semester, and there's even better news than that, and I can't wait to tell you, and I am so happy we won," she said, in what may have been the fastest run-on sentence in any language.

Mary and I rushed to the lobby to get details. Jing, as it turned out, got detained because the top officer—the one Jimmy's buddies needed for approval—was not in the office to sign-off on her extension.

Jing was told to spend the night in the consulate building until he was located. Their building had two floors of dormitory-style, temporary sleeping quarters for detainees.

She could not call because, for security purposes, there was no Wi Fi. She was incredulous, of course. "Can you imagine? Couldn't use my iPhone. Felt like I was in the Ming Dynasty all over again. Killer. Really."

A fate worse than death, we agreed. And where was this official whose signature was needed?

"He was at the game!" said Jing. "That was bummer. Half the office was there. I had to be the only Chinese person in Chicago not at the game."

Now we were perfectly poised. Not only had the Colonials polished off No. 1 seeded Milton, they had done it without their good luck charm.

The remainder of the off-day—Saturday—was strictly down time. In the early afternoon, Harrison and Mesquite each got access to Wintrust Arena for 90 minutes of practice time.

We took Jing to our session. Charley and the players were excited to see the "cabbage." Or as Wang Chen, our unofficial team leader, put it: "All things are difficult before they are easy."

Apparently, it's an old Chinese proverb. Deep. Well, maybe you had to be there.

The workout was upbeat. Everyone was feeling good after the victory. The coach's concern was to make sure we did not get overconfident and, of course, make sure no one twisted an ankle in the session.

That night a team dinner was held at Willy's restaurant in Chinatown. When word got out, we became the center of attention—dozens of curiosity seekers watched our party through the window.

The highlight? Willy announced a new menu item in our honor, the "Harrison College Wok Tossed Veggies in Honey and Black Bean Glaze."

"Very popular already," he said. "Now even more popular. I like it for this honor. Many ingredients go into making it good. Just like the basketball team. There are many different people from all over playing together."

This drew a big cheer.

Billy Jack's practice session was vanilla, too. He and his assistant ran some light, generic drills. He, like every coach in America, was paranoid. No way in hell was he going to be specific in the Buckaroo workout. No telling who might be watching.

"Keep it light, Jimmy," he told his assistant. "This is about getting a feel for the court, finding the soft spots on the floor, bounces off the rim, sight lines, and all that stuff."

The coach was especially easy on Luke, bruised and exhausted from enforcer role against Stratford. The coach was undecided whether to unleash him again Harrison's big center in the final.

The biggest challenge was keeping his players focused the rest of the day. No problem with Ollie, though. He stayed in his room, venturing only as far as the hotel lobby to buy sports magazines in the gift shop. No way was he ready to test Chicago's judicial system a second time.

Oscar went for a short afternoon visit in the National Mexican-American Museum of Art in the Pilsen neighborhood. He managed to talk several teammates in joining him. Otherwise, no one ventured more than a few blocks from the hotel.

Billy Jack returned to Wintrust that evening to watch the cheerleading finals, which Merrilou's squad won in a showdown with Kentucky Wesleyan. No contest, really. Their acrobatic routines would've drawn "10s" in Olympic gymnastics.

Big Hal and Ruthie could hardly contain themselves over their daughter's accomplishment. Ruthie had to wipe away tears.

Billy Jack acted enthused, but his mind was elsewhere throughout the competition. He did admire the footwork, however. He took out a piece of paper and scribbled a few notes.

Hey, you never knew where you might find good ideas.

104

The Final

ALL EYES IN the Wintrust Arena, plus those of a national TV audience, followed one, final sequence in the championship game.

From deep in a corner of the basketball court 25 feet from the hoop, Jimmy Bradley launched a soft-sailing, 3-point jump shot. The high-arching basketball was inches above the outstretched fingers of Luke Hodges.

Harrison teammate Yang Lu had spotted an open Bradley, who signaled for the ball. A momentary slip on his catch allowed the 7-foot-1 Hodges to close the gap, his running leap with long, outstretched arms an awesome sight—like a swooping pterosaur from Jurassic Park.

There was little left in his liftoff after his tournament efforts, but Luke gave it the supreme effort. This shot would decide the NCAA championship in a furious contest witnessed by the largest audience—counting TV—ever to watch an athletic event at this level.

There were two ticks remaining on the arena clock. Mesquite led 92-90, but a basket would hand victory to Harrison after battling back from a 13-point deficit with less than two minutes remaining. There would be no time for the Buckaroos to answer.

Bradley, a Hoosier hotshot if ever there was one, practiced this shot a million times. Not on a hoop attached to a barn on a farm, but in the gymnasium of his hometown Kokomo YMCA. His form was perfect. He calmly let fly with the jumper.

It was likely the NCAA would never again see a windup like this, and not just because the outcome was decided so dramatically. There had been close games before in the finals, even overtimes.

Consider: One finalist had basketball players on rodeo scholarships. A little over a year ago, it lost a game to an earthquake. Its ranks included a Mexican-American who taught Spanish-language plays to teammates, a parolee playing with an assumed identity, a convert to Islam from Detroit by way of Tennessee, a Special Forces veteran with multiple tours in Iraq, and an inner-city kid from Los Angeles who beat a rap in criminal court on a game day.

Then consider this: The other finalist had four transfer players on the floor from China, with a fifth Chinese teammate sitting on the bench with five fouls while their can't-fail, good luck charm—a "cabbage" named Jing—watched from press row.

And now the outcome of this stewpot was in the hands of the only traditional student-athlete on the floor, a freshman from Kokomo. He missed.

The ball clanged off the hoop's front lip, caromed 90 degrees inward, hit the back rim, bounced tantalizingly up and down and around the rim several more times, and finally fell outside instead of inside the metal basket.

There was a second of total silence before the roar.

The action had been non-stop, with 100% effort by Mesquite and Harrison players alike—and with a national champion cheerleader squad to hike the entertainment level.

Players dove for loose balls, tumbled into sideline seats, and committed few turnovers, making some brilliant, NBA-worthy passes. The coaches countered each other with chess-like moves. Charley's last one, shifting Bradley to his Panda unit, ignited the late rally with his long-distance shots until the final effort.

Whether you pulled for the unknown Buckaroos from Oklahoma or the foreign Colonials from Indiana, everyone in the arena knew they had witnessed something special.

More special than they realized.

School's out

THIS WAS RARE. Whitey's was empty. Of course, it was only 11 o'clock on a Monday morning in May. Hopefully no one saw me enter and thought I was desperate for a drink.

"What brings you here, stranger," said Whitey, looking up from the beer steins he was drying. "Long time, no see. Where's your better half?"

The school year ended a week ago. Mary was gone. Like everyone else. Nothing moves faster or disappears more quickly than college faculty in the summer.

Already she was in Arizona to start another border adventure. "She's pretty special," he said. "You better hang on to her." The thought crossed my mind, was the response.

I was just back from O'Hare Airport in Chicago, leading the escort of our Chinese students to their United Airlines flight to Beijing. They were anxious to get home and be reunited with families.

This was tearful for some, but truth be told, I could not help but feel a bit liberated. I pretty much was non-stop for a year. There were two trips to China, arrangements to make, and, oh yeah, courses to teach. My passport was dog-eared. Now this adventure was over.

Jing and her brother, Zhang, were especially anxious to see their parents. Somehow, I knew I'd be seeing her again. Already she and

Willy were discussing some future role for her in Chinatown working for the Chamber of Commerce, which could lead to full-time residency.

Now I could concentrate fully on future Harrison class projects, my day job. I was on good paper with President Casey and, as long as he didn't jump ship for a better job, the school seemed headed for a renaissance of sorts. He was a builder, not a manager, and I strongly suspected he wanted to see how far he could take the college.

I wanted to be part of it. Hell, I *was* part of it.

When I returned to my car in the O'Hare airport parking lot, I seriously debated whether I should head west for Iowa City to visit old Airport pals. Or, should I return to Harrison? This freedom felt very, very good.

I chose Door No. 2. Following a night in a motel in Indy—as far as I could make it with my eyes open—the return trip got completed the next morning.

I drove straight to Whitey's for early lunch, an obvious stalling tactic to delay needed household chores. The milk in my refrigerator, long past expiration, probably was sour cream. The bread most likely had grown hair.

"Haven't seen you much since the tournament," said Whitey. "Everyone's still talking about it. Real proud, too. Just a damned shame you guys didn't win. We were the better team. They were a bunch of shitkickers, you ask me."

"Yeah, well, no one remembers who finished second, I guess, but maybe they'll remember our guys," was my best comeback. "Hard to forget them. We raised some eyebrows, though. That's for sure."

In the long view, Harrison *was* a winner.

After viewing the raw, first take of Hu's documentary sent to me and President Casey, there were no doubts the college would become popular in China after it aired there. This would be good for enrollment and Chinese students in America typically were cash on the barrelhead.

Ka-ching.

The Harrison trustees, meeting in a week, already were on the case. President Casey was asked to prepare a proposal to start an international business major with special emphasis on China. In a hurry.

This would mean hiring more faculty, an enrollment increase, and need for a new dormitory. The hot rumor: Several large Indiana corporations, interested in establishing larger Asian footprints, were ready with substantial funding to help expansion.

I don't know if the president was tossing a bone to me, or what, but he also hinted the possibility—a little farther down the road—of creating a Masters of Fine Arts (MFA) degree in creative writing. This would be the school's first graduate-level program. Low overhead, he said.

To me, this meant Dean Brunk, who still had not mastered the fine art of email, was headed for the pasture. Or emeritus status, as they like to call it in academia. No roadblocks there.

Our exchange ties with Xiamen University remained firm. We were in touch with my old pal Wang (Bunny) Li, dean of the communications college. She was eager for this partnership to grow.

Harrison's title run was big news on the Xiamen campus, where the Final Four games were shown live on an outdoor, big screen not far from the courts where my old faculty team played. They drew huge crowds.

Some entrepreneurial Xiamen students cleaned up selling bootleg Harrison t-shirts. If I checked into it, pretty sure Jing's fingerprints might be found.

Most likely Bunny would pay us a visit in the next school year, and bring a delegation. College professors and administrators were the same all over the world. They jumped at paid junkets. Looked good on the CV.

Meanwhile, it was our turn next autumn to send a dozen students to Xiamen. This turned into a very spirited competition on our campus in weeks that followed the tournament.

I was pleased to see Kate McDonald's name on the final list. Jing would make sure her buddy had a good time. Would Nate pay his daughter a visit? I wasn't sure if China was ready for the Holy Roller's main man. I'd pay to see that.

"Yeah, well, a lot of good things may come out of this, but next season's going to be a letdown in basketball," said Whitey. "That's what my customers talk about. That freshman, Jimmy Bradley, is good, but that's about it. Felt sorry for him at the end."

Everyone on the Eagle unit will return, I pointed out. They saw lots of action, too, thanks to Charley's platooning. Also, this year's success was bound to help recruiting. And who knows? Maybe we'll get some more good Chinese players down the road.

This much was for sure: The cupboard would not be bare as Mesquite's.

"How so?" asked Whitey.

"You didn't hear? Its coach, that Burns guy, Billy Jack, is gone. Took a job elsewhere. He was gone, and his office cleared out a week after Chicago. It's back to bucking broncos and bull riding for the Buckaroos."

Billy Jack accepted an offer from Waco State to lead its program into Division 1 status. The rumor was that he accepted before the championship game with us.

If he could get a forlorn program like Mesquite's—in a desolate region of the country, no less—to the NCAA's Final Four, no telling what he could do now.

"No more making chicken salad out of chicken shit," as he explained it to Merrilou, who was part of the package. She would take charge of the cheerleaders. A paid gig for her, too.

The coach figured to also bring JJ with him as a transfer. He'd be back in Texas, with his parole near an end. He could enroll and play under his real name, Jumbo. He could drop using brother Jimbo's identity.

Better yet: Since there was no record of him playing a season for Mesquite under his real name, Jumbo thus had another year of eligibility to burn. Sweet.

The remaining members of Mesquite's championship team? They would stay in Beaver Junction, where Jimmy decided to remain as Billy Jack's replacement.

"So, you see, Whitey, in the end everything worked out OK."

Whitey added, "Yeah, but their kids couldn't have been nicer than ours. Before leaving, the Chinese all came out here and had a little farewell gathering. Thanked me for my hospitality, too. Nice of them.

"That little Jing was in charge. Hard to believe it was less than a year ago they poked their heads through my door for the first time. I'm putting egg rolls on my menu in their honor."

About the author

Mike Conklin is a career journalist, first covering sports in the small Iowa town where he was raised before a long run as a sportswriter for The Chicago Tribune. He touched every base: features, news, daily columnist, editor and, on the side, Basketball Weekly correspondent. He left The Tribune to join the full-time faculty at DePaul University, where he taught and helped found the journalism department. Sports and higher ed? Two target-rich worlds for a writer.